FIRST TIME FATHER

THE MODERN GUIDE FOR EXPECTING DADS TO
EASILY NAVIGATE PREGNANCY AND PREPARE
EFFECTIVELY

EVERETT WOODS

IMAGINE TREEHOUSE

Just for you

A FREE GIFT TO MY READERS

Learn 7 Simple Time Management
Strategies for Busy Parents, Just Visit

ImagineTreehouse.com

CONTENTS

Introduction   vii

1. Smile – You're going to be a Father!   1
2. A Quick Overview of What's   18
   Happening in the Womb
3. The First Pregnancy Trimester   30
4. The Second Pregnancy Trimester   56
5. The Third Pregnancy Trimester   68
6. Catching the baby! (aka Labor and   83
   Delivery)
7. Taking Care of the Family Economy   126
8. Ensuring Your and Your Partner's Well-   141
   Being
9. Welcome to the First Week of   158
   Fatherhood!
10. Conclusion   175
11. Resources To Dig Deeper   182

INTRODUCTION

"THE QUALITY OF A FATHER CAN BE SEEN IN
THE GOALS, DREAMS, AND ASPIRATIONS HE
SETS NOT ONLY FOR HIMSELF, BUT FOR HIS
FAMILY."
- REED MARKAM

One day, you're just driving down the freeway. It's Friday afternoon after an exhausting week at work, and you can't wait for the weekend to begin. You're making plans in your head: where should you and the wife go tonight? Maybe the bar? The movies? Karaoke? Dinner and dancing? Impromptu road trip? Hmmm...

anything goes! We're young, in love, and the world is our oyster!!!

And then, in a flash, that world is gone and will *never* come back again. You walk in the door, still excited about a prospective evening of either relaxation or self-indulgence, and you hear those words you'll never unhear: "I am pregnant." And there it is!!! These three words have the power to evoke a flurry of emotions in human beings: they can ignite volcanos, cause earthquakes, calm the storms, and suppress tsunamis.

While just a few moments ago, you could only think about the next few hours, now you're thinking about forever. You feel excited, thrilled, scared, unprepared and responsible at the same time. Whether you fall into the tribe of first-time dads or are someone who has lived this experience before, you always have mixed feelings about becoming a parent.

So many feelings...none right, none wrong. There's no script for this moment. Of course, for the most part, you're happy and joyous. Still, when practicality hits, it becomes challenging to keep happiness intact. Becoming a parent is not a solo trip – you and your partner are together in this. It's a joint venture that you have to take care of together.

And now you're wondering...feverishly questioning, wanting to know where you stand in this whole new world you've just been thrust into? Sure, the mother has the bigger responsibility of pregnancy and giving birth to a child - *your* child! Still, your presence and support are equally important. As they say, "Knowledge is power." If you have an idea about the whole drill from start to finish, your role as a parent becomes much simpler (not easier!) and exciting. You can do this!

It starts with a vision of the future. No matter how different every father, mother, and child can be, there's not one parent who doesn't want better for their child than they had. That's why you're here...thumbing through this book, trying to create a perfect life for someone you've never even met...a life that's better than your own. That's your first step to being not only an amazing father but an invaluable support for the mother of your unborn baby.

I'm Everett Woods, an educator specializing in teaching couples who are expecting a baby. Originally from Chicago, I currently live with my wife Amy, a registered nurse, and our daughter in Washington, DC, preparing to have another child.

As an optimistic person, I celebrate being a parent and consider it one of the biggest blessings of my life. However, I well recall the trials and tribulations of trying to get pregnant as well as navigating pregnancy, birth, and raising small children. Each stage brings a roller coaster of emotions. I wanted to play an active role in parenting, and partnered with my wife, Amy, to research parenting styles, philosophies, and methods every day. Now, I am passionate about sharing the strategies that get us through - and encouraging fellow Dads.

My goal in sharing this book is to propel your confidence in your preparation for a new little one. What you're about to go through, I went through too. I remember feeling that sense of security grow during the challenges we encountered during pregnancy that prepared me to bring a new baby into the world. This book is designed to bring that sense of security into your life.

So, what should you expect at the beginning of the pregnancy, and what do you need to know as a father? How vital is it to have a clear vision of how to support your pregnant partner? To do this effectively, you must have as much information as possible regarding emotional and physical changes a woman experiences during her pregnancy....not just from textbooks and experts but from real people who have lived through real situations—fathers and mothers who've not only experienced successes but failures and comebacks, as well.

Even after learning, reading, studying, memorizing, and applying every bit of information you can absorb, there is so much more to the pregnancy process. Every parent's journey is unique. Don't be afraid, and certainly don't get down on yourself. You may find yourself in analysis paralysis...what do I do? When? How? Why? This book is written to be an in-depth but reader-friendly guide to being the best father and partner you can be throughout this process.

As I mentioned earlier, pregnancy is not a one-size-fits-all, cookie-cutter situation. Every pregnancy, every mother, every father, and every child is unique. Unfortunately, no definitive guide exists; rather, there is a wealth of medical and anecdotal information from people worldwide recounting situations that you may see and what opportunities and solutions there are to help you succeed. That said, no matter how much you know and prepare, mistakes still happen. And that's ok!

Most moms have crazy pregnancy or birth stories they proudly share like badges of honor. Celebrities are no exception:

Katy Perry: "Your belly isn't the only thing that may grow when you're carrying a baby! My hands are swollen, my feet are starting to swell. It's starting to get to that point." She also shared her intense and newfound craving for hot sauce. "I like, literally, never cared for spice, and now, I have to carry Tabasco sauce in my purse."

Mandy Moore: In her third trimester, Mandy took to Instagram to ask her followers, "is anyone else suddenly nauseous, exhausted, and weepy? What the heck?" The next day, Mandy was feeling more herself, sharing that "hormones are no joke!"

Khloé Kardashian: "At the beginning, the first trimester is the worst, and no one knows you're pregnant yet, and you feel the most uncomfortable," Kardashian said of her pregnancy with baby True. "I think once people know you're pregnant, you get all the excuses. Hopefully, I look pregnant, not just fat. It's hard for me to breathe right now."

You may fear the unknown or worry about making a mistake. No matter how afraid you are, your partner is most likely just as scared, if not more. And while your life has already begun down an entirely new path, your body won't be changing and your hormones will not be out of whack. Your partner will be the one managing the brunt of the labor (no pun intended!). Still, you can ease that burden by doing exactly what you're doing now—caring enough to learn and to grow with her (again, no pun intended!). You have already figured out the most important thing you can do: support your partner's needs during this exciting, but challenging time.

In addition to worrying about how you will affect your baby's life, you may also be concerned about how this tiny human will affect your time, sleep patterns, and (up-to-this-moment) social life. Do you feel you are not adequately prepared for this monumental change about to hit your home like a Tasmanian Devil? What's more, this creature will depend wholly on you for feeding, burping, bathing, changing diapers, and knowing the proper way to carry him.

According to Rob Williams, Chief Executive of The Fatherhood Institute, expectant fathers should try to involve themselves in the daily routine as much as possible when the baby arrives. "Do as much as you can – housework, cooking, nappy changing, holding the baby. Fathers are great at everything except breastfeeding. If a father sees this responsibility as part of his role as well as his partner's, they are more likely to end up with a shared approach to parenting." This starts in pregnancy. The time I spent going to appointments with Amy, picking out baby gear and learning about childbirth allowed me to hit the ground running once our daughter arrived.

Will you be an expert father after reading this? Well... maybe not an *expert*, per se, but you'll certainly have more confidence to handle what comes at you. The time you spend learning will give you security. Security in the knowledge that you and your partner are working as a team with the end goal of bringing home a happy, healthy, and fully functional human being. After reading this book, you will feel capable of handling the huge responsibility of becoming a father. You'll be given all the vital information on pregnancy – from tackling physical and emotional challenges to taking care of your newborn in her first days of life and making necessary life changes to accommodate a new member of the family.

Additionally, I'll share useful knowledge on how to support both your partner and your child. You'll be able to extend your love and care for your partner into action by supporting them throughout their pregnancy and postpartum. You'll gain knowledge of the numerous options available to secure your finances, and gain tips and advice on taking care of your mental health and fitness.

Lastly, I'll leave you with the best advice I ever received from my father: Expect the best but prepare for the worst. Read on to develop your roadmap for your survival over the next 9 months.

SMILE – YOU'RE GOING TO BE A FATHER!

You're here! Since the introduction didn't scare you away, I can only assume you're in it to win it, so I'll just jump right in. In this chapter, we will focus on what to expect in the early stages of pregnancy, starting with early pregnancy symptoms and strategic advice on how to handle these changes.

For some time, it's been just you and your partner. Free to come and go as you please. Spur of the moment long weekends, coast-hopping vacations, and even sleeping in on weekends are all going to take a back seat to the little bundle of love that the stork has targeted for delivery.

Pregnancy can be both a physical and mental challenge for the mom-to-be. Her body is creating a human life;

no small feat. As you've already gleaned from the instant you learned that you'll be welcoming a new life into your family, fatherhood is a major identity transition that can bring uncertainty along with excitement. As the non-birthing partner, Dad may feel sidelined until the baby arrives. By taking an active role in preparing for the baby and supporting Mom during pregnancy, you will be better positioned to tackle your new role with confidence.

Becoming a parent is one of the biggest blessings bestowed upon us humans, but it also requires filling a large pair of shoes. Up to this point in life, you may have enjoyed taking things as they come. It's best to make some preparations when you're going to be a father, especially if it's your firstborn! The nine months leading up to birth are there for a reason. They give Mom's body the time it needs to turn food, water and oxygen into a human being. You'd be wise to take advantage of that time as well, and there's plenty for you to do.

Supporting someone through pregnancy, labor and newborn baby care is an important job. Whether you are the baby's father, the pregnant woman's partner or are supporting a single mother-to-be, you have a crucial role in ensuring she gets the support she needs during this life-changing time. There is an abundance of good information for pregnant women – what to expect, what is happening physically, psychologically and emotionally, practically minute-by-minute. But for the men (or partners), there isn't a lot.

WHAT THE MOMS-TO-BE SHOULD EXPECT?

If you're a pregnant mom, you're probably getting lots of attention—even occasionally having complete strangers ask personal questions and touch your belly when you're out and about. But dads-to-be? Far less visible. The truth is that fathers have an important role to play, too—of course after the baby is born, but during pregnancy as well.

Pregnancy is not just a period of creating a tiny human; expecting mothers undergo a transformation and come out forever changed. Though fascinating, pregnancy doesn't really start off well for most mothers. Quite often, moms-to-be experience a host of difficult symptoms throughout the first trimester. In this period, however, the new parents may not be prepared to share their good news with the world, which severely limits their options for external support. She may have only you, Dad, until you both make the move to enlighten your family and friends. While difficult at times, this is a perfect opportunity for you and your partner to strengthen your bond during these last months of living as two (at least for 18 years!).

Dads who play an active role during pregnancy lower moms' stress levels. And lower stress means a healthier environment for your growing baby. Research shows that dads who are involved during pregnancy are more likely to remain involved once the baby is born —with great results. Kids with dads who are involved in their upbringing tend to do better socially, emotionally, and academically than kids with uninvolved fathers.

I remember scanning the Kindle website and scrolling through hundreds of books with big bold titles designed to catch our attention about what to expect when we're expecting. "Which one is the best?" we asked ourselves, reading the back of each book and getting more confused and information overload with each blurb.

We both wanted to know everything there is to know about parenting but honestly, the only way that you will ever know about 360 degrees of parenting is when you actually become a parent yourself. Even then, every day is a new day with its own struggles, mistakes and mulligans.

No book, magazine, or website can fully prepare you for the pregnancy. It can only coach, mentor, advise, and guide you through what the author has experienced. As you experience new things filled with trial and error, you become more confident about your decisions and you learn to go of perfection because you know that if you don't, fatherhood will just be a never-ending battle.

Here's are just a few things that moms-to-be can expect in the early stage of pregnancy (Don't worry...I'll go into more detail in later chapters!):

Missed period - Once conception has happened, the woman's body produces hormones that stop ovulation and the shedding of her uterus lining. This means that the cycle has stopped and she won't have period again until after the baby is born.

Raised basal body temperature – Hot flashes are common! Have a fan on hand for her and a blanket for you!

Smell sensitivity – Take care with cooking, candles, colognes, and other items that may affect her differently now that she's with child. These smells, though tame prior to her pregnancy, may now cause nausea and distress.

Breast changes – Painful swelling and tenderness can happen almost immediately for some. For others, it may begin by the halfway mark and worsen until well after the birth.

Fatigue – Be supportive of your partner. She may need more naps than usual, or even just a sit-down break. She is now sharing her energy with 2 people instead of just herself. Tiredness can also cause irritability. As your partner gets further along in her pregnancy sleeping is likely to become more and more uncomfortable. The baby's weight can put pressure on her spine, back muscles, intestines, bladder and major blood vessels, leading to decreased circulation, pain and a frequent need to urinate. This can make it difficult to sleep. Getting your partner a full body pillow, giving her back rubs and brewing soothing teas can all help.

Spotting – Though you want to be vigilant with heavier bleeding, know that in the first 12 weeks of pregnancy, slight vaginal bleeding is common and generally not a cause for concern.

Changes in cervical mucus – During the first weeks of her pregnancy, cervical mucus may change in color and consistency, and she may notice stickier, white, or yellow mucus, known as leucorrhea. This is completely normal!

Frequent urination – make sure pathways to the bathroom are clear, because middle of the night potty trips are going to be inevitable!

Mood swings - Not every expecting woman will experience rapid changes in mood, but those who do fluctuate from fury to fear to bliss will have to learn to roll with the punches — while resisting the urge to actually knock anyone out along the way. The good news is that the mood swings are temporary. While there are certainly several factors contributing to mood swings, the biggest culprit is a sudden surge in pregnancy hormones. During the early days of gestation, a woman experiences a veritable flood of estrogen and progesterone, and these can do a number on one's state of mental health.

Bloating - One possible cause of bloating during pregnancy is hormonal fluctuation. Pregnancy hormones relax the womb, and the digestive muscles also relax, slowing digestion. This can lead to constipation, a common challenge for pregnant women, and constipation can cause a person to feel bloated.

Heartburn and indigestion - Pregnancy increases the pregnant woman's risk of heartburn or acid reflux. In the first trimester, muscles in the esophagus push food more slowly into the stomach which then takes longer to empty. This process allows the body more time to absorb nutrients for the fetus, but it can also result in heartburn. In the third trimester, the growth of the baby can push the stomach out of its normal position, which can also lead to heartburn.

Morning sickness and nausea - Despite its name, morning sickness is not always restricted to the morning. It can strike at any point during the day or night and symptoms of morning sickness include nausea, with or without vomiting. Most women who experience morning sickness usually feel nauseous for a short time each day and may vomit once or twice. In more severe cases of morning sickness, nausea can last several hours each day and vomiting occurs more frequently. Be ready to stop the car often!

Food aversions - Sometimes women will have food cravings, and some women will experience a food aversion — a strong dislike of certain foods. Food aversions during pregnancy are completely normal, though unpleasant. They often start during the first trimester and go away by the second, though it's possible that her appetite could be out of whack until your baby is born. Common food aversions during pregnancy include meat, eggs, dairy products, spicy foods, foods with strong smells, and coffee. While these appetite changes might be quite common, they can make healthy eating during pregnancy a challenge.

Excess saliva - Saliva build-up in the mouth early in pregnancy, sometimes called ptyalism gravidarum, is one of those strange pregnancy symptoms some moms-to-be experience, though it's relatively rare and most often reported by women who also have morning sickness.

WHAT THE DADS-TO-BE SHOULD EXPECT?

Pregnancy isn't just a roller coaster ride for the mothers – the fathers are equally in the adventure. And sometimes "what to expect when you're expecting" doesn't cover everything! "Pregnant" fathers often complain of weight gain, morning sickness, food cravings, and backaches — symptoms that are said to be common in the pregnant woman but not the father-to-be! But don't worry. Though you don't hear about it as often, these symptoms happen all the time. Perhaps it's Nature's little way to ensure a bit of empathy for what your partner is going through.

How about this quandary? Your pregnant partner has every right and reason for her midnight requests for Ben & Jerry's or pancakes or whatever else she (and the baby) are in the mood for. But what's your excuse? You're not eating for two like the mom-to-be. Don't be alarmed! You're not alone in sharing pregnancy symptoms. You and a wealth of non-pregnant parents-to-be are unfortunately in the middle of couvade syndrome, a French term meaning "sympathetic pregnancy" AKA "we're pregnant." According to GoodTherapy.org, "studies have found varying rates in different parts of the world, but the most recent statistics suggest Couvade syndrome occurs in about 25% to 52% of men in the United States who have pregnant partners."

Many men experience some sort of physical symptoms when their partners are pregnant, sometimes gaining up to 30 pounds during pregnancy! These changes are most likely the result of men's desire to participate — to be more a part of the pregnancy, which will, after all, transform their life. They're preparing for their new role as a father.

According to an article by Ariel Ramchandani entitled "She Got Pregnant. His Body Changed Too," there is no population of males who are excused from potential Couvade syndrome. But the condition reveals how transformative fatherhood is—and how society misunderstands that. Ramchandani shares that in 2019, during his wife's second pregnancy, Washington Wizards NBA player, Bradley Beal, went public about how food cravings and weight gain left him drained and ashamed when his partner was pregnant.

Beal notes that "I was up at 3, 4 o'clock in the morning eating ice cream when I shouldn't have been eating ice cream...because momma was pregnant and I had the exact same symptoms." Men also post similar experiences on Reddit's forum. "There are days that I wake up violently ill and I can't keep anything down all morning," one poster wrote. "I don't feel sick otherwise, just the vomiting. So much vomiting ... Maybe it's all in my head." In 2016, Karlos Williams, an NFL player for the Buffalo Bills at the time, said he had been slowed down by extra weight gain after the birth of his fourth child. He attributed his poor in-game performance to "the injury of pregnancy."

If society sees parenting only as the domain of women, the act is undervalued as both a responsibility and a rite of passage for men too. Increasing the dialogue around men's experience and how transformative the experience is directly bearing on women's access to support. In fact, all parents face higher expectations today. Viewed this way, a phantom pregnancy is neither empathy pain for a partner nor a subconscious attempt to hog the familial spotlight, but a physical surfacing of the dissonance between what a modern dad experiences and what society expects. Ramchandani postulates that perhaps society will one day look back on the diagnosis of couvade, with its amorphous symptoms and psychosomatic roots, the way people retrospectively think of how doctors diagnosed women with hysteria. As society changes, our medical frameworks should too.

Psychologist Daniel Singley, a therapist who runs the Center for Men's Excellence asserts that many couvade symptoms are limited by society's approach to men's mental health. "As a society, we punish men and boys for having depression or anxiety or really any sort of mental-health issues," Singley shares. "Some men will somaticize and turn depression into 'I just feel like there's a heaviness on me or gastrointestinal problems. My stomach's upset. I get migraines. I have muscle tension.'" After the birth of his own child, Singley experienced unwanted intrusive thoughts, which can be a hallmark of postpartum depression in women.

Today's father-to-be is so much more involved than in the I Love Lucy and Leave it to Beaver days. The roles played by past generations of fathers often don't give new dads clear direction. Kidding from friends and coworkers may lead to increased anxiety, even if the ribbing is good natured. Unfortunately, some outdated gender assumptions persist in society, which celebrates a vision of men as high-testosterone and aggressive, and that's inconsistent with the parenting role that best serves kids.

Men don't always think to tell their doctors that they are fathers-to-be, missing out on an opportunity to discuss how to manage stress. Today's dads spend more time caring for their children than their fathers and grandfathers did. They recognize the value of sharing the everyday tasks of raising children—from diapering to discipline. Dads' choices, and their voices, matter— to them, to moms, and to their kids.

I say all of this to stress the fact that anxiety among new fathers is to be expected and may be amplified as you attend prenatal exams which might leave you feeling awkward, questioning how you should behave, and asking yourself questions like: Where should I stand? What should I look at? How should I feel about this other person touching and intimately examining my partner? Can I ask questions without appearing stupid? Yes! Ask questions! This shows you care, which decreases your partner's stress and yours as well.

As you read earlier, mood swings are a huge part of pregnancy for the mom-to-be, but it's not just pregnant women who experience pregnancy mood swings. Many men also experience emotional changes during pregnancy, such as moodiness and depression. These symptoms may be linked to their worries about change, the loss of routine or even losing their partner's love and affection once the baby is born.

Having honest conversation and open communication with your partner may help alleviate your worries and may help resolve them, too. There's another benefit to talking: While you are being more open about your concerns, you're also exploring what kind of dad you'd like to become.

Some things you can do to calm both your anxiety and hers include attending as many of her prenatal checkups and childbirth education classes as you can. Remember that these are a time for you as well as for her to ask questions and share your fears which helps to prevent feelings of isolation, which can damage a relationship.

Read on to find out what to expect when you've just found out that you're soon going to be a dad.

Anxiety - Almost all fathers-to-be have some kind of anxiety (and I believe that those who claim they're worry-free are simply not paying attention). The most common concerns are financial security, changes in the marital relationship, the impending lack of sex, the loss of free time and personal space and, as I pointed out, fears of danger to the mom, the baby, or the dad himself.

Nausea – These symptoms follow a chronological pattern similar to the mother's experience, beginning in the first trimester of pregnancy, before temporarily disappearing in the second and then re-appearing in the final trimester. They can even extend into the period after the baby is born.

Mood Swings - New demands and responsibilities during pregnancy and the postpartum period often cause major changes in a father's life, too. It's important to understand what risk factors can affect the development of depression and mood swings.

Changes in sexual appetite - Some men find sex during pregnancy an incredible turn-on. Others... Well, it's not even on their radar. Both are perfectly natural responses. Where you stand on the issue depends on a lot of factors, but one thing is pretty much guaranteed: when your partner is pregnant your sex life will change. We'll talk more about that later.

Weight gain - Gaining sympathy weight during pregnancy is completely normal. Even though you're not carrying a baby, you may well gain weight over the 9-month journey to fatherhood. This "sympathy weight" isn't a myth. In fact, a 2009 study found that men reportedly gained an average of 14 pounds during their partner's pregnancy. Amy and I usually only bring healthy food home, but during bouts of nausea and food aversions our pantry was suddenly stocked with crackers, chips and candy. Needless to say, this didn't help matters in the fitness department.

Aches and pains – Although your body may not be undergoing the same hormonal changes as the mom-to-be, your experience shouldn't be ignored. Many men have experienced a variety of sympathy pains throughout this time, including toothaches, headaches, and backaches.

. . .

PREGNANCY is a roller coaster ride not just for the mothers but also for their male partners. As exciting as it is, becoming a father is a huge responsibility that demands your utmost attention and care. Having the knowledge of what to expect in pregnancy beforehand can rule out the surprise factor and make you more prepared for your role as a father. If you are like most expectant fathers, you are both excited and anxious about this big step in the lives of you and your partner. You can help your partner by understanding the changes she is going through and by being a prepared and supportive father-to-be.

In the following chapters, I will guide you through the most vital points in surviving this pregnancy, including why the father's role is important to a healthy pregnancy, the physical and emotional changes your partner will experience during pregnancy, sex during and after pregnancy, what happens during prenatal care visits, how to help during labor and delivery, and what fathers can do after the baby is born. Your job as a father begins long before your baby is born. Research has shown that women with supportive partners have fewer health problems in pregnancy and more positive feelings about their changing bodies.

2

A QUICK OVERVIEW OF WHAT'S HAPPENING IN THE WOMB

Here we go! You've just found out that you're going to be a dad. It's perfectly normal for you and your partner to feel nervous and unprepared. That said, if you have some idea of what to expect throughout the pregnancy, you can very well handle the journey of becoming parents. Of the many challenges during pregnancy, keeping track of when the baby is due is one of the most important ones. You want to do your math right to make the necessary adjustments, both personally and professionally. But there's no need for you to exert yourself; finding the due date is pretty basic and doesn't need a mathematician to figure that out. In this chapter, you will be given a glance into the whole pregnancy period, allowing dads-to-be to stay informed about important pregnancy dates and intervals.

A Quick Sneak Peek into the Pregnancy Journey

How many weeks are in pregnancy?

Pregnancy normally lasts from 37 weeks to 42 weeks from the first day of the last menstrual period.

How many weeks are in a trimester, and how many trimesters are in a pregnancy?

Pregnancy is divided into three trimesters: First trimester - Conception to 12 weeks. Second trimester – 12 to 24 weeks. Third trimester – 24 to 40 weeks.

Is pregnancy 9 or 10 months long?

40 weeks of pregnancy are counted as nine months. But wait ... there are four weeks in a month, which would make 40 weeks 10 months. Right? Not exactly. Four weeks is 28 days, but months (except for February, of course) have 30 or 31 days, making each month about 4.3 weeks long.

How many weeks is a full-term pregnancy?

If the mother to be is carrying a single baby, full-term pregnancy is between the start of 39 weeks up to the end of 40 weeks, with viability at approximately 28 weeks.

PREGNANCY MONTHS TO WEEKS CHART:

If these explanations have your head spinning, here's a simple breakdown of approximately how the weeks, months, and trimesters are counted in pregnancy.

TRIMESTER 1

- **Month 1:** Weeks 1 to 4
- **Month 2:** Weeks 5 to 8
- **Month 3:** Weeks 9 to 13

TRIMESTER 2

- **Month 4:** Weeks 14 to 17
- **Month 5:** Weeks 18 to 22
- **Month 6:** Weeks 23 to 27

TRIMESTER 3

- **Month 7:** Weeks 28 to 31

- **Month 8:** Weeks 32 to 35
- **Month 9:** Weeks 36 to 40

How do I know what week of pregnancy my partner is in currently?

Her doctor says she's 15 weeks pregnant, but you're also being told that she's in week 16. Which is right? Short answer: both. In both cases, the due date is the same — it's the language referring to it that's different. How many weeks into pregnancy you are is slightly different from how many weeks pregnant you are. If you're in week 16, you're 15 weeks and some days pregnant. Fifteen full weeks have gone by, but not 16 weeks, so people say that you're both 15 weeks pregnant and in week 16 of pregnancy.

How do we calculate the due date?

Still haven't checked in with the doc about your baby's estimated due date? It's calculated counting from the first day of your partner's last menstrual period (LMP) instead of the day she conceived. So, try to remember the first day of her LMP and add 40 weeks to that.

. . .

Why is pregnancy calculated from the last period?

Why start the clock on pregnancy before sperm even meets egg (and, actually, before your partner's ovary even dropped the fated egg that made your baby)? Because it can be hard to know which day conception actually happened, the LMP is simply a more reliable day to date pregnancy.

Supporting your pregnant partner from day one

The news of becoming parents is overwhelming, and thus, it needs to be talked out thoroughly to ensure that you and your family stay healthy and positive throughout the process of bringing a new life into the world. Some stress is unavoidable, but by staying informed, you can help your partner navigate pregnancy smoothly and keep herself and the baby healthy. By communicating, you serve to strengthen the bond between the two of you, which forms a baseline for a healthy and beneficial partnership for the next 9 months + 18 years. And remember, true communication involves as much, if not more, active listening as talking.

. . .

Who should we tell first?

In many ways, it is harder to tell close family and friends that you are pregnant than people you do not know as well. Therefore, it may be worth planning who you will tell first about your pregnancy and how you will do it. Close friends and family members may prefer to be told personally, and some family members, such as parents, may also expect to be some of the first people to be told.

How do we tell them?

It is worth remembering that if you announce your pregnancy on social media, you may have little control over who views your announcement and when. Be aware that such public announcements may draw significant attention, personal stories, and advice, which may or may not be invited and wanted. Even announcements made in confidence may become widely known since people love to share news like this when it's posted online.

A good reason to hold off on sharing your great news till the 12th week or later is the potential of a miscarriage, which unfortunately is quite common. It is hard to know how many miscarriages take place because sometimes a miscarriage can happen before the mother knows she is pregnant. The estimated figure, according to Tommys.com, is that miscarriage happens in around 1 in 4 recognized pregnancies, with 85% of those happening in the first trimester (weeks 1 to 12). A 'late' miscarriage, which is much less common, may occur between weeks 13 to 24 of pregnancy.

Our OB told us that miscarriage risk drops significantly once a healthy fetal heartbeat can be confirmed via ultrasound at around 7 weeks. We chose to share our news with family after an early ultrasound, and with a wider circle after the first trimester.

AGE MAKES A DIFFERENCE TO RISK LEVELS:

- If a woman is under 30, she has a 1 in 10 chance of miscarriage
- If a woman is between 35 and 39, she has a 2 in 10 chance of miscarriage
- If a woman is over 45, she has a 5 in 10 chance of miscarriage.

So when should we tell our loved ones? It's completely up to you and your partner! Many couples choose to confide in a selected few for moral support and others feel comfortable sharing more widely - it's a personal choice.

KNOW YOUR HR BENEFITS — MATERNITY & PATERNITY LEAVE

An important detail that may be overlooked in the onslaught of excitement and emotions are the hard, cold facts about HR benefits. Here are vital questions you and your partner should be asking your employers:

- Is there pay for maternity/paternity leave? For how long?
- Must PTO be used for doctors' visits?
- Is additional time off available if necessary?
- What are the organization's pregnancy and family-related benefits?
- Who will oversee specific job duties during maternity leave, and will the same role be available following a return from leave?
- Is remote work a possibility?

- Will consistent updates be available during this time?
- What paperwork needs to be signed before leave begins?
- Will retirement and other contributions continue during maternity leave?
- How is the new baby added to the insurance policy?

SUPPORTING YOUR PARTNER THROUGHOUT HER PREGNANCY

Be patient: Pregnant women go through a lot, both physically and emotionally. It's hard for men to grasp, but her hormones can hugely influence her mood and behavior. Be patient and understanding...remember that it is not your partner; it is the hormones talking.

Don't react, just listen: When your partner tells you what upsets her, just listen without passing judgment or giving a solution. Put your phone away, look her in the eyes and be 100% present for her. Sometimes she just needs someone that will listen.

Satisfy her cravings: Pregnant women have bizarre cravings. Men should not be surprised if they are asked to make a 'sliced pickle and salt and vinegar crisp' sandwich. Do not question the cravings; just accept the oddest combinations as part of pregnant life. Satisfying her cravings will make her feel loved.

Read lots of books and blogs: There is so much information on pregnancy, babies, and children. Gender equality has closed the gap on which parent looks after the baby. Modern men now help their partners on every step of the journey.

Take holidays together: Couples should consider taking a relaxing mini-vacation or two while expecting. There is nothing that provides more comfort than some quality couple time. A trip away or even a fun staycation weekend will help remind you why you're bringing a new life into your family – to share in your love.

Compliment her regularly: There is nothing more radiant than the glow of a pregnant woman, but she may not feel this way. Men need to remind their partner how loved she is. This should not be a one-off but a daily occurrence. A simple compliment can help a pregnant woman to regain her confidence.

Go to appointments: Of course, with COVID-19 restrictions in place, this isn't always possible at the moment, but when it is allowed, men should try to go to every appointment they can!

Put your social life second: Prioritizing your relationship may mean putting social plans on hold if your partner doesn't feel up for attending.

Change things up: The fatigue is **real** during the first 12 weeks, so you may need to take over household chores like cooking and cleaning.

You'll find some more tips on how to support and care for your partner and the relationship in later chapters.

Having an idea beforehand about pregnancy prepares parents to know what they should expect. You don't need strong analytical or calculation skills to determine the due date; a simple calendar is good enough to determine when the baby is due.

Nausea, dizziness, joint aches, strange aversions to once-loved foods and smells... the first trimester is a time of unimaginable physical upheaval for your partner. Whether it's money, listening, work/life balance, substance abuse, or something else – every relationship has issues. The strain and profound change of pregnancy give extra fuel to your usual arguments, fights, and issues. It pays to work on your relationship before getting pregnant.

As a friend of mine put it: men have their own pregnancy too, and a big part of it is learning how and when to put the needs of your family before your own.

3

THE FIRST PREGNANCY TRIMESTER

T hough your partner is pregnant, there's no baby in her belly yet, and the baby is still two weeks away from making its way into her mother's belly. While you're not the one who's always tired and suddenly loves pickles and peanut butter, you can feel more connected to your baby when you know what's happening.

WEEK-BY-WEEK GUIDE: FORMATION OF THE BABY

MONTH 1: WEEK 1-4

Week 1: Not pregnant yet / Week 2: Ovulation and fertilization. No, there's no baby yet, but these next two weeks, your partner is gearing up for ovulation — the moment the egg destined to turn into your child breaks out of one of the ovaries and makes its way down the fallopian tube and ultimately to her uterus. On the way, it'll be met by the sperm that fertilizes it.

Week 3: Sperm meets the egg. Congratulations! Sperm has met egg, and that single cell is now rapidly dividing into a microscopic ball of cells that will emerge as your baby in about nine months (give or take).

Week 4: Pregnancy Testing. While you both wait for her to take a pregnancy test, maybe give any not-so-great habits an overhaul. Some important advice for women and men during pregnancy: Quit if you're a smoker — second-hand smoke is extremely bad for the health of mamas- and babies-to-be. Another important tip? Make sure Mom-to-be is taking a high-quality prenatal vitamin – do your own research on the best options for her needs. Some resources to get you started are included in the final section of this book. Getting a positive pregnancy test doesn't mean that the baby has already arrived in the mother's belly. It takes a few weeks before the baby shows up.

· · ·

The Placenta

So, you want to know all about the placenta...What is it? What does it do? We will talk about the placenta more in-depth later in this chapter. For now, a few basics. The placenta begins to form soon after the embryo implants in the uterus. Maternal and fetal blood vessels lie very close to one another inside the placenta, allowing nutrients, oxygen, and waste to transfer back and forth. The placenta grows like a tree, forming branches that divide into smaller and smaller ones. About three weeks after fertilization, these blood vessels join to form the baby's circulatory system, and the heart begins to beat.

Eating for Two!

According to medicalnewstoday.com, to help prevent illnesses and other complications during a pregnancy, women should avoid:

- Soft, mold-ripened cheese: Cheeses such as brie, feta, camembert and cojito carry a risk of listeria contamination. Listeria is a group of bacteria that can cause potentially fatal infections in pregnant people and their babies. While most cheese in the U.S. is pasteurized which reduces risk, listeria could possibly grow after pasteurization. For this reason, Amy felt most comfortable avoiding all soft cheese.

- Deli meats can also harbor listeria, but can be ok if heated until steaming.
- Seafood that contains mercury: Avoid shark, swordfish, and marlin, or keep the intake to an absolute minimum. Tuna is ok, but in moderation – think once a week. Salmon, cod, tilapia and other small fish is perfectly safe and good for baby's brain development. Refer to the FDA's website for a pregnancy-safe fish guide.
- Uncooked or partially cooked meats: Opt for thoroughly cooked meats (use a meat thermometer) to avoid risk of listeria or toxoplasmosis, a parasite which is expecially harmful to unborn babies.
- Uncooked shellfish: This is due to a risk of bacterial or viral contamination, which can cause food poisoning.
- Raw eggs: Avoid these and any foods that contain them.
- Unwashed, raw fruits and veggies: Because

produce can become contaminated by other food along its journey, always wash raw fruits and vegetables thoroughly.

DEALING WITH FATIGUE, FRUSTRATION, AND FEAR

According to several studies, a high proportion of first-time pregnant women report experiencing some fear during pregnancy. In fact, health concerns are much more common among pregnant women than in the general population. Sources of concern vary depending on the trimester. For instance, in the first trimester, the fear of losing the baby is more common, whereas in the third trimester, the fear of childbirth increases.

Although some women believe that their fears are not justified, others believe that they have reason to worry. Some go so far as to say that their fears are sometimes positive. A certain level of anxiety can be beneficial, as it encourages the expectant mother to avoid behaviors that put the baby at risk. Anxiety also signals an increased sense of responsibility, which can help the expectant mother plan for the child's arrival.

Ultimately, the goal is not to completely eliminate anxiety during pregnancy, but to learn how to manage it to avoid any negative effects and prevent the development of anxiety disorders.

So tired!!! Baby isn't even here yet, and already your partner's exhausted. It's hard to drag her weary body out of bed each morning. By dinnertime, all she wants to do is plop back down and climb underneath the covers. Fatigue is one of the first signs of pregnancy. It can keep nagging throughout most of the 9 months until delivery but is most common during the first and third trimesters.

To manage this fatigue, try to make sure your partner takes lots of rest breaks during the day and scale back on activities and duties that aren't required. It may help to join her for regular exercise - go outside, take walks, or keep the blood moving with a favorite workout. Finally, eating a balanced diet and drinking plenty of water can keep blood sugar steady and make fatigue a little more manageable.

FREQUENT URINATION – IS THAT A PROBLEM?

First-time moms worry that frequent urination could be a sign of a problem. While it can be an inconvenience, the increased need to pee is typical for many women during pregnancy. However, if frequent urination is accompanied by pain, any blood in the urine, fever, or chills, that would cause concern. These symptoms could signify a urinary tract infection, which is common in pregnancy, and your partner should see her family doctor to get tested and treated.

FEELINGS OF DAD-TO-BE

For many men, the news that you're going to be a dad can bring about a mix of feelings – some positive, some not so much. You could feel panic, anxiety, shock, or numbness at first. It isn't wrong to feel this way – there might be reasons for these reactions, or you might just need time to adjust. Most men get into it eventually, but it might not feel real until after your baby is born. This is when you can get involved and start being a dad.

FEELING 'LEFT OUT' AT PREGNANCY APPOINTMENTS?

Some of your experiences with pregnancy services might not be what you expect. Although services are getting better at including men in prenatal care, sometimes the system forgets that men are interested and want to be part of things. It's easy to feel invisible if a health professional talks as if your partner is the only one expecting a baby.

NOT GETTING EXCITED ABOUT THE PREGNANCY — YET.

You might be waiting to make it past the 12-week scan that checks whether your baby is ok before you let yourself get excited about the pregnancy. Many people go public with their pregnancy news at 12 weeks, and others wait until the 20-week scan. If you're waiting to clear these checks before you let your excitement show, it might look like you're not interested in the pregnancy. In this case, you could reassure your partner by telling her that you're happy about the pregnancy, but you want to know everything is ok before you get too excited.

UNPLANNED PREGNANCY?

Perhaps the pregnancy is unplanned – perhaps you don't want the pregnancy at all – but the mother has decided to go ahead. This is a very difficult situation, and it's normal to have strong emotions. It's good to take some time to think about what you're feeling. It can also help to learn more about becoming a dad. If you're no longer in a relationship with the mother, it's usually best for your child if you can still be involved. It might help to learn more about co-parenting.

THINGS YOU CAN DO

If you have mixed feelings about the pregnancy, try talking to other dads and expectant dads as a way of getting your head around the change. Accept what you're feeling rather than ignoring it or trying to 'fix' it. If your partner is upset that you're not getting into the pregnancy, reassure her that it's common for dads to feel this way at first. It does NOT mean that you won't be a wonderful father. It just means that you need extra space and attention to process your emotions.

MONTH 2: WEEKS 5-8

Week 5: The baby is the size of an orange seed now, and your partner may be showing early signs, too — like achy, tender breasts and bone-crushing fatigue. The evolving neural tube will eventually become the central nervous system (brain and spinal cord). One chore you can officially take over? Cleaning the litter box if you have a cat. Cat poop can contain parasites and transmit a disease called toxoplasmosis, which, while rare, could harm unborn babies.

Week 6: Look! The baby is there! Nausea can kick in right about now, but the term "morning sickness" is misleading — many moms-to-be feel queasy the whole darn day. The baby is now known as an embryo. It is around 3 mm in length. By this stage, it is secreting special hormones that prevent the mother from having a menstrual period.

Week 7: The baby has a face. Your partner's sense of smell can rival a bloodhound's at this point, which means any offending odor can send her running to the bathroom. The heart is beating and can be detected on an early ultrasound! The embryo has developed its placenta and amniotic sac. The placenta is burrowing into the uterine wall to access oxygen and nutrients from the mother's bloodstream.

Week 8: Formation of limbs. Your partner may be experiencing more food aversions these days, as morning sickness tends to peak around this time. The embryo is now around 1.3 cm in length. The rapidly growing spinal cord looks like a tail, and the head is disproportionately large (don't worry, he or she will get cuter by the day!).

ALMONDS AS A SUPERFOOD FOR PREGNANT WOMEN

Being pregnant is a moment of excitement and celebration for everyone in the family. Especially for mom to be, this journey can be overwhelming. With nausea, tiredness, mood swings and hunger cues, the body of pregnant women becomes vulnerable to certain foods. During our pregnancies, our doctor suggested almonds, one of the best such tiny nutrition-based superfoods packed with key nutrients like magnesium, calcium, dietary fiber, protein, omega 3 fatty acids, and vitamin E.

So, add some love, nuttiness, and sweetness to your partner's beautiful and magical journey of becoming a mother. Sprinkle a few slivers of almonds into her milkshake, oatmeal, or by ordering that big jar of almond butter. FYI: According to NHS (National Health Service), women can eat nuts or foods containing nuts during pregnancy until and unless advised not to by a healthcare professional or due to a nut allergy.

MORNING SICKNESS: IS IT LEGIT?

Nausea that often accompanies the early part of pregnancy (and can last longer) can strike at any time of the day. Nice. So, it's your job to help her out in any way you can. I've included some basic facts and pointers to guide you along your way in this tricky process.

WHAT IS MORNING SICKNESS?

Morning sickness is nausea during pregnancy, which may or may not be accompanied by vomiting. More than half of pregnant women have morning sickness, especially during the first trimester. Despite its name, you can have morning sickness at any time of day.

. . .

WHEN DOES IT START? HOW LONG DOES IT LAST?

Morning sickness usually begins a few weeks after conception and lasts through the 3rd or 4th month. Morning sickness can start as early as a few weeks after conception and be the first sign of pregnancy. Morning sickness usually begins at some point during the first trimester and often resolves at 14–16 weeks of pregnancy.

Symptoms

- Nausea with or without vomiting during the first trimester feels like motion sickness.
- Nausea that comes on in the morning resurfaces at any time or goes on all day.
- Feeling sick from smelling certain foods and other odors (food aversions).
- Nausea after eating, especially spicy foods.
- Nausea or vomiting brought on by heat and severe salivation

Causes: There's no one cause of morning sickness during pregnancy, and severity varies among women. During the first few weeks of pregnancy, increased hormone levels are the most common causes. Reduced blood sugar is another common cause of morning sickness.

Remedies: Here are some great tips and tricks you can suggest to your partner from www.betterhealth.vic.gov.au:

- Don't take drugs of any kind unless your doctor knows you are pregnant and has prescribed specific medications.
- Eat a few dry crackers or plain sweet biscuits before getting out of bed in the morning.
- Don't eat anything that you suspect will make you nauseous. In general, high-carbohydrate meals are well tolerated.
- Eat small meals regularly, as an empty stomach tends to trigger nausea.
- Drink as much as you can manage, or try sucking on ice cubes.
- Vitamin B6 supplements can be useful, but doses above 200 mg per day can be harmful. As your doctor.
- Wear loose clothes that don't constrict your abdomen.

- Moving around may aggravate morning sickness. Rest whenever possible.

Foods for morning sickness

(https:www.obgynofatlanta.com/nutrition-for-nausea-during-pregnancy):

- Saltine Crackers
- Milk Shakes
- Melba Toast/Graham Crackers
- Grape Juice
- Bagels – Plain or with Cream Cheese
- Papaya Juice
- Toast/Cheese Toast
- Apricot Juice
- Peanut Butter
- Apple Juice
- Peeled Apples/Apple Sauce/Watermelon
- Gatorade
- Oatmeal/Grits
- Lemonade
- Dry Cereals
- Ginger Tea
- Rice/Noodles/Baked or Boiled Potatoes
- Hi-C Punch
- Oodles of Noodles

- Ginger Ale
- Macaroni and Cheese
- 7-Up
- Scrambled Eggs
- Sprite
- Sherbert/Ice Pops
- Coke
- Pretzels/Pop Corn
- Ginger Snaps
- Tuna/Chicken – Baked or Grilled

CAN MORNING SICKNESS HARM YOUR BABY?

Some women are concerned that vomiting may threaten their unborn baby. Vomiting and retching may strain the abdominal muscles and cause localized aching and soreness, but the physical mechanics of vomiting won't harm the baby. Rest assured that at this early stage in the pregnancy, the baby will get the nutrition needed from mom-to-be even if she can barely keep anything down. However, staying hydrated is important and severe morning sickness can and should be treated professionally.

So when should the doctor be called?

Call the doctor right away if you're pregnant and have any of these symptoms: nausea that lasts throughout the day, making it impossible to eat or drink; vomiting three to four times per day or not being to keep anything in the stomach; brownish vomit or vomit with blood or streaks of blood in it.

Does no morning sickness mean something bad?

No! Count your blessings! About 70% of pregnant women get morning sickness. In about 3%, nausea and vomiting can be severe. My wife was one of the luckier ones who only experienced mild and intermittent nausea. However, when she felt great, she tended to worry about the health of the pregnancy. In fact, her experience is 100% normal and our daughter was growing just fine!

Your Baby on the Screen: Scans and Tests During the First Trimester

Things you can do

Go to the first scan. Make the appointment with your partner at a time and day that suits you too, if possible. If the scan shows something unexpected, support your partner. Recognize your feelings, too; talk with someone you trust.

First-trimester pregnancy scan

Your partner will be offered her first ultrasound scan at 6-12 weeks of pregnancy which checks that your baby is growing in the right place, if your baby is developing as expected, and how many babies are present. This scan helps health professionals work out your baby's age and estimated due date and is part of the check on the chance of your baby having a condition like Down syndrome.

First-trimester screening tests

Your health professional will talk with you and your partner about screening tests for chromosomal abnormalities and other conditions in the first trimester.

WHAT IS NIPT?

Noninvasive prenatal testing (NIPT), sometimes called noninvasive prenatal screening (NIPS), is a method of determining the risk that the fetus will be born with certain genetic abnormalities. This testing analyzes small fragments of DNA that are circulating in a pregnant woman's blood. I suggest asking your doctor about NIPT if they don't bring it up, as it is a way to assess the genetic health of the pregnancy without a risky procedure. Heads up that this testing can also reveal the sex of the baby, so you will want to let your doctor know if you want to keep that news a surprise.

OTHER SCANS - FIRST TRIMESTER SCREENING TESTS

- Early Pregnancy Scan.
- Nuchal Translucency Scan.
- Early Blood Tests.

- Chorionic Villus Sampling.
- Non-Invasive Prenatal Testing.
- Fetal Anomaly Scan.
- Fetal Echocardiography

MISCARRIAGE OR HEALTH PROBLEMS AT 12 WEEKS

Although most pregnancies are straightforward and progress without problems, there's a chance the scan could show that your embryo is no longer alive. Miscarriage is common and can be devastating.

Remember – miscarriage is not your or your partner's fault! It's usually a genetic flaw that spontaneously happens when sperm meets egg. According to the Mayo Clinic, early miscarriage is the most common pregnancy complication in the United States, affecting up to 1 million women each year. It can occur due to a range of issues a patient cannot control, such as chromosomal abnormalities in the embryo – the cause of approximately half of all miscarriages. Research suggests some women find comfort and support on social platforms such as Instagram after a miscarriage.

Connecting with others who have been there can help them surface their emotions and feel less isolated.

Unfortunately, our first pregnancy did end in miscarriage, which was discovered in the first scan and was a total shock for us. We shared our grief with family and close friends, and had many share that they had also experienced a miscarriage and gone on to have a healthy child. These stories gave us hope through the sadness, and we're now one of those couples who went on to have a healthy child. For most couples, miscarriage, while devastating, is a one-time event.

MONTH 3: WEEKS 9-13

Week 9: Finally, I see my baby! The eyes, mouth and tongue are forming. The tiny muscles allow the embryo to start moving about. Blood cells are being made by the embryo's liver. You partner's breasts and nipples may be growing, but they're also probably super tender. You may have to go easy when you're having sex, as even the slightest and gentlest touch may be too much now.

Week 10: Embryo turns into a fetus. The embryo is now known as a fetus and is about 2.5 cm in length. All of the bodily organs are formed. The hands and feet, which previously looked like nubs or paddles, are now evolving fingers and toes. The brain is active and has brain waves. Your partner will be going to the doctor regularly for prenatal checkups right up until labor. If you're able, you'll want to go with her on some (if not all) of these appointments.

Week 11: Adios, webbed limbs. Hello, fingers and toes! Chances are, she has to go all the time now, thanks to the hormones triggering a more frequent urine flow and more efficient kidneys. Teeth are budding inside the gums. The tiny heart is developing further.

Week 12: Formation of vital organs. The fingers and toes are recognizable, but still stuck together with webs of skin. Some mamas-to-be find that pregnancy fatigue, nausea, and bloat put them off sex for a while. If your partner falls into this category, reconnect in other ways.

Week 13: Closure of the first trimester. The fetus can swim about quite vigorously. It is now more than 7 cm in length. At this time you may feel a little left out...that's normal! She may not even realize she's leaving you out, or she may be hesitant to "burn out" the topic this early in the pregnancy. Set her at ease by bringing it up yourself.

Placenta – When, where, and how?

When does the placenta form? The placenta starts developing very early on in pregnancy at about week 4. Seven or eight days after a sperm fertilizes an egg, a mass of cells — the earliest form of an embryo — implants into the uterus wall. Over the next two months, the placenta develops.

Where is the placenta? In most pregnancies, the placenta is located in the upper part of the uterus, however sometimes, the placenta attaches lower in the uterus or on the front uterine wall.

How much does the placenta weigh? How much the placenta weighs depends on how far along you are in your pregnancy. At 10 to 12 weeks of pregnancy, the average placenta weighs nearly 2 ounces. By 18 to 20 weeks, the placenta weighs about 5 ounces.

Placenta problems in pregnancy. To remain fully functioning and growing at the right pace, a placenta requires the same healthy lifestyle as the baby. That means smoking and using illegal drugs are off-limits as well as harmful drugs such as alcohol and marijuana (even if she has a marijuana card!).

Potential Problems with the placenta include:

- Enlarged placenta, a placenta that's disproportionately bigger than normal
- Anterior placenta, a placenta that's on the front (anterior) side of the uterus – this is less of a problem than a variation, but it makes it more difficult to feel baby's kicks
- Placenta previa, a placenta that covers part or all of the cervix
- Placental abruption, the early separation of the placenta from the uterine wall
- Placenta accreta, a placenta that's attached too firmly to the uterine wall

Delivering the placenta: When your baby is born, the last thing on the mind of prospective parents is likely the placenta that remains inside the uterus. However, after your baby arrives, your partner will need to push out this organ.

WHAT DO WE DO WITH THE PLACENTA AFTER THE BIRTH?

Many people feel squeamish when placentas are discussed, but they are truly amazing as your body has grown an entirely new organ to sustain your baby. In fact, in other cultures, such as Maori in New Zealand, the placenta is treated with so much respect that it is returned to the land in a burial ceremony.

Some cultures even eat the placenta! According to verywellfamily.com, the practice of placentophagia, eating the placenta, is practiced all over world. There are even meal-like recipes for cooking placentas, including placenta stew, placenta lasagna, power drinks with blended placenta and others. Some mothers have been reported to eat placenta raw.

Even if you are turned off by the thought of keeping the placenta, try to have a look at this amazing organ that has kept your baby alive for all those months inside your partner.

The first trimester of pregnancy can feel quite odd. So many things are changing and yet there's little evidence of an actual baby! All the focus is on your pregnant partner but it's ok to reach out to friends and family if you would like support, too. Be empathic to your partner. Her body is changing fast and she may be feeling really unwell. You can't fix that, but don't underestimate how much you can help, both practically and also just by listening and being there for her.

Most of all, try to enjoy this special time together, and hang on in there – the second trimester, where most pregnant people feel much better, is just around the corner! Your support as a partner and a dad is irreplaceable in helping your pregnant partner sail through the difficulties that arise during this time a bit more easily.

4

THE SECOND PREGNANCY
TRIMESTER

Y es! You and your partner have done it. You have made it through that scary, tiring first trimester and you are into the second. As well as your partner feeling and looking more pregnant during these weeks, she might seem a little more energetic than before. This will come as a great relief to you both if you have been struggling with sickness, tiredness or anxiety about getting through the first trimester.

As you both progress through the second trimester of pregnancy, you can expect various changes in your partner's body. While it may be intimidating, rest assured that everything's normal and is happening at its own pace. This section will discuss the development of a baby during the second trimester, the emotional and physical challenges that women go through during this period, and how their partners can help them during this time.

Your partner's second trimester starts in week 14 of pregnancy and lasts through the end of week 27. Now that all the major organs and systems have formed in the fetus, the following six months will be spent growing. The weight of the fetus will multiply more than seven times over the next few months, as the fetus becomes a baby that can survive outside of the uterus. Your baby is very, very busy in the second trimester. By week 18 of pregnancy, he weighs about as much as a chicken breast, and can even yawn and hiccup. By the end of the second trimester, he will be about 13 to 16 inches long and weighs about 2 to 3 pounds.

The good news is that most women find the second trimester to be the easiest and most enjoyable part of their pregnancy. What's more, you may feel more comfortable sharing the news more widely, and can benefit from excitement and support from your community. However, it's still important to maintain (or get back into) healthy behaviors — like eating right and exercising — to ensure the rest of the pregnancy goes smoothly.

. . .

MONTH 4: WEEK 14-17

Week 14: A visible baby bump. Finally, people start to notice. Be ready for lots of questions! When the baby begins to get attention depends on a lot of factors, including the mom's body type and whether or not it's her first pregnancy. If she's not showing yet, no worries - she will be soon! By now your baby might be almost 3 1/2 inches (87 millimeters) long from crown to rump and weigh about 1 1/2 ounces (45 grams).

Week 15: Baby gets hair! Agonizing over all the choices as you brainstorm baby names? Consider these tips: Go through the alphabet a few dozen times (or more) as you try on names for size. My wife and I used a shared list app to jot down ideas as they came to mind. Bone development continues and will soon become visible on ultrasound images. Your baby's scalp hair pattern also is forming.

Week 16: Butterflies in her stomach — baby starts moving. Mama may or may not feel slight "flutters." Are *your* moods going up and down, too? No wonder — you're probably feeling conflicting emotions from excitement. Talk out all those fears and anxieties. Your baby's limb movements are becoming coordinated and can be detected during ultrasound exams. However, these movements are still too slight to be felt by you. By now your baby might be more than 4 1/2 inches (120 millimeters) long from crown to rump and weigh close to 4 ounces (110 grams).

Week 17: Here comes the snore! Who knew? Pregnancy hormones are stuffing up your partner's nose, and snoring while sleeping can be one of the side effects. (Don't worry, it's temporary.) Your baby is becoming more active in the amniotic sac, rolling and flipping. His or her heart is pumping about 100 pints of blood each day.

MONTH 5: WEEK 18-22

Week 18: Is it a prince or a princess? You're the best partner you know how to be, and one of the things you're doing to earn that position is to play chef more than usual. Your baby's ears begin to stand out on the sides of his or her head. Your baby might begin to hear sounds. The eyes are beginning to face forward. Your baby's digestive system has started working.

Week 19: Time to do some shopping. Getting misty-eyed at the sight of baby onesies? Blame your hormones. Yes, even the manliest of macho men get a higher estrogen level and drop in testosterone during pregnancy. During this time, the baby is developing a protective coating, a greasy, cheese like coating called vernix caseosa begins to cover your baby. The vernix caseosa helps protect your baby's delicate skin from abrasions, chapping and hardening that can result from exposure to amniotic fluid.

Week 20: Milestone achieved! This week is the level 2 ultrasound, the 20-week anatomy scan. This much-more-detailed ultrasound shows your partner's practitioner how your baby is developing. By now your baby might be about 6 1/3 inches (160 millimeters) long from crown to rump and weigh more than 11 ounces (320 grams).

Week 21: Getting a kick out of kicking. Your partner may be feeling those first wiggles, kicks, and flutters that are a sign that there's an actual little being in there. It's about one of the most thrilling pregnancy milestones there is. It won't be long before you, Dad, will be feeling the life inside your partner, as well. We'll discuss more on that later. Twenty-one weeks into your pregnancy, or 19 weeks after conception, your baby is completely covered with a fine, downy hair called lanugo.

Week 22: Breaking the 1-pound mark. Afraid of hurting the baby when you are having sex? As long as your partner's practitioner has given her the green light and you both feel up for it, go ahead and have fun. It will be important to maintain your romantic connection after your baby arrives, and rest assured that he is safe and has no idea what's happening. Your baby's eyebrows and hair are visible. By now your baby might be 7 1/2 inches (190 millimeters) long from crown to rump and weigh about 1 pound (460 grams).

Scanning at Week 20

Purpose for the scan: The 20-week scan can happen anywhere between 18 and 20 weeks. This detailed ultrasound looks at your baby's body parts, including internal organs, checks the location of the placenta, and picks up any obvious problems. If you want to find out the sex of your baby, this is the time to ask - sex identification in this scan is about 95% accurate.

What you can see in the scan: At the 20-week scan, you'll probably see your baby's heart beating, the curve of baby's spine, baby's face, and baby's arms waving and legs kicking. There might even be some cute thumb-sucking.

Miscarriage or health problems in week 20: It's rare to lose a pregnancy after about 13 weeks. The overall risk of miscarriage after this time is about 3%.

Things you can do: Decide with your partner whether you want to find out your baby's sex. Going to the ultrasound is one of the few chances you'll get to see your baby before birth.

BUILDING YOUR BABY REGISTRY

As much as it's a practical way to prepare for your new addition, setting up a baby registry is also an exciting rite of passage. It's fun to dream about what it will be like once your little one is finally home, to imagine him (or her) wearing those teeny-tiny newborn diapers, to envision the perfect theme for your new nursery.... Setting up a registry makes it all feel real. (And, come on, going to the store and shooting products with the scanner gun is just plain awesome.)

A baby registry is a giant wish list of all the swag parents-to-be want in preparation of their newest addition. These items are typically gifted at showers (or at a smaller celebration if it's a second or third baby) and help set new parents up because—let's face it—having a baby isn't cheap. And since people will want to spoil you and the baby anyway, you might as well point them in the right direction by cataloging exactly what you want.

Registries generally pack a roster of asks, from large-ticket items like a stroller, monitors or a high-tech bassinet, to little-but-necessary—items, like washcloths, wipes, pacifiers and that diaper cream you'll be very grateful for later.

You can register for gifts online, in person or both. Every store is different, but most have a checklist to guide you, loaded with suggested items, along with a quantity for each. The registry keeps track of what you've asked for and what's been purchased already, to avoid duplicates from your gift givers.

According to www.todaysparent.com, Just like buying a car, going into a store to register is a great way to test drive products you're interested in and to be introduced to things you didn't even know you needed. Hashing out your concerns and questions with people who live and breathe baby products will help you determine what items will fit your life.

From hundreds of baby bags to even more choices for car seats and bedding and everything baby-related, there is no right or wrong choice. And don't even get me started on car seats that attach to strollers! We went to every baby store in town trying to find the perfect stroller and car seat combination. You see, car seats can clip into strollers – giving you the ninja-like ability to transfer a sleeping baby from car to stroller without waking her. Not every stroller is compatible with every car seat, and there's a maddening number of choices for each.

We found that every store had its own brands and styles of car seats and strollers...anywhere from your basic Ford Fiesta package to your Rolls Royce ride. There were just so many choices! We ended up getting a middle of the road stroller from JC Penney and a car seat with a great safety rating in Consumer Reports magazine. No need to go overboard – the baby won't even know if it's enjoying the ride in a top-of-the-line stroller or a simpler and more inexpensive Walmart or Target brand.

No matter which decisions you're struggling with, I suggest asking friends and family. There's so much information online that, for us, it was most helpful to hear directly from other parents we knew.

MONTH 6: WEEK 23-27

Week 23: Braxton Hicks contractions. Braxton Hicks contractions are mild, irregular contractions during pregnancy. They feel like tightness in the abdomen. Some women feel a lot of Braxton Hicks contractions, while some women don't feel them at all. They typically last less than 30 seconds, and they can be uncomfortable but rarely painful. If your partner is having trouble nodding off, show some solidarity. Surprise her with a full-body pillow so she can get comfy and sleep.

Your baby may recognize sounds, like your voice, and if you talk or sing or read to your baby, you may even feel her move in response.

Week 24: Your baby can hear you; time to bond! Your baby-to-be is the size of a grapefruit now. And those little ears can now pick up the sounds of the outside world – including your voice! Put on your favorite soothing songs and play them every so often (I give myself – and this tip - the credit for my daughter's love of classic rock!).

Your baby's muscles continue to grow and may start to have hair on its head. The baby's lungs are fully formed but not ready to breathe outside the womb yet. It's about 12 inches long and may weigh a little more than 1 pound.

Week 25: Getting there! Your partner has probably been able to feel the baby's movement for a few weeks now, but by week 25 or 26, you might be able to feel your little one from the outside, too.

Your baby's nervous system is developing quickly. The nervous system is the brain, spinal cord and nerves. It helps your baby move, think and feel. Your baby adds more fat to its body, which makes the skin look smooth and less wrinkly.

Week 26: Can you see me?! As the second trimester draws to a close, you might start to wonder how you'll do during labor and delivery.

Your baby's body is making melanin, a substance that gives it skin color and protects its skin from the sun after birth and the lungs start to make surfactant. This substance helps your baby's lungs get ready to breathe.

Week 27: Goodbye, second trimester! Your baby is doing lots of kicking and stretching as the lungs and nervous system continue to develop. As your partner's bump gets bigger, the skin stretches and becomes dryer and itchier. So, take over and rub shea butter or coconut-scented cream all over her belly. It's a sexy and oh-so-soothing way to pamper your partner.

The second trimester involves the first appearance of your baby and its growth from a speck on the screen to a one-pound mini-me of you and your partner. This period is quite overwhelming both physically and emotionally, as the baby has now taken a tangible form. Hence, it's a stage where you can proudly say – We are parents!

5

THE THIRD PREGNANCY TRIMESTER

The last months of pregnancy are the most exciting. You are more than halfway through the wait to become parents. Passions are high, and you and (especially!) your partner have never been more impatient to get that baby out in the world. This chapter will take you through an exciting pregnancy journey as you coast along the last trimester. This chapter discusses the baby's growth during weeks 28-42, also known as the third or final trimester of the pregnancy.

MONTH 7: WEEK 28-31

Week 28: Your little one can blink, even dream!
Your baby now has eyelashes and can open and close its

eyes. Your baby is about 14 inches long and weighs about 2½ pounds.

Bottle feed or breastfeed? By the third trimester, your partner may already have made up her mind, or she may appreciate talking it through with you. Together, do your homework — you'll find out if you haven't already heard that breastfeeding offers many benefits to the health of the baby, but some moms have difficulty breastfeeding or prefer formula.

The La Leche League (LLL) (www.llli.org) is an international organization with a primary focus on the personal one-to-one sharing of information and encouragement that provides a new parent with the confidence they need to breastfeed their baby.

Week 29: Baby's saying "cheese"! Your partner's not the only one having trouble falling asleep. You may be tossing and turning as you think about all the things you two won't be able to do once the baby arrives — hopping in the car to go hiking, taking up roller skating, or even just going out at night whenever the urge hits.

Your baby starts to put on weight fast! In the last 2½ months of pregnancy, your baby gains about half of its birthweight. Be sure to cook your partner healthy foods so your baby has the nutrients it needs to grow.

Week 30: Bigger brain for a big guy. With ten weeks left, give or take, childbirth might be on her mind a lot more now. If you haven't signed up for a childbirth class, contact your OB physician, your doula, the hospital where your partner will deliver and enroll in one, or websites specializing in obstetric support, such as www.whattoexpect.com, www.mayoclinic.org, and www.pregnancysupport.com, to name a few. You might also want to discuss a birth plan — does she want an epidural, what positions does she want to labor in, who will cut the cord?

During this time, your baby begins to lose the lanugo, the soft fine hair that covers its body. The baby also may have a good amount of hair on its head (but maybe not...don't be surprised either way!).

Week 31: Your little coconut. Your baby's the size of coconut this week, putting more of a strain on your partner's body. To accommodate that growing belly, she has to shift her posture, which might make her klutzy. Your baby's brain grows and develops quickly and its brain can now help control body heat.

COMPLICATIONS DURING THE FINAL TRIMESTER

Just like an accident on the road, while you may not expect it, you can still be prepared. If your partner experiences complications, try to keep a level head. In many cases things will resolve without serious problems, but it can be a terrifying time.

We had a scare when ultrasound measurements showed concerns about our daughter's head size. Due to her breech position, it was difficult to get a good measurement and we had to go for extra scans and non-stress tests, which measure the baby's heart rate, to ensure she was growing ok. Thankfully, she turned around into the head-down position at the last moment and we could confirm that she was healthy.

Other issues, such as gestational diabetes, have scary potential outcomes but can be well managed with lifestyle changes and medication. Don't be afraid to ask your doctor all of your questions or call their office frequently to ensure you fully understand what to do and maintain your peace of mind.

Common Complications: If your partner has a high-risk pregnancy or health concerns, the third trimester might not be the exciting countdown you expected. Common pregnancy complications in the third trimester include pre-eclampsia, gestational diabetes, too much or too little fluid around your baby, your baby not growing as expected or growing too quickly, your baby sitting in an unusual position, or a problem with the placenta.

Getting information: If your partner has a pregnancy complication, you'll want to find out everything you can. If you keep a list of questions, it will help you focus your conversations with health professionals.

Getting support: As with any stressful life situation, support from trusted family and friends can play a big part in helping you and your partner cope with pregnancy complications. If people offer to help, it's ok to say yes.

Things you can do: Try to accept offers of practical help, and take things one day at a time. Share what you're going through with a family member or friend.

Month 8: Week 32-35

Week 32 - Organs are fully formed. Quick! When's the last time you saw your primary care practitioner? If you can't remember, it's time to schedule an appointment or at least call to see if your immunizations are up to date. Dads and any other future caregivers, like grandparents, need to make sure their whooping cough, flu, and COVID vaccines are up to date.

Your baby now weighs about 1.7kg (3.7lb) and is as long as a kale leaf, around 42.4cm (16.7in) from head (crown) to heel. From 32 weeks, babies born early have a good chance of surviving and thriving, although they will need help to breathe at first. This is because their lungs won't be fully developed until just before birth.

Week 33: A pint of amniotic acid, please! While you're scheduling your doctor visit, it's time for the two of you to go shopping for your baby's doctor. Hospitals require a pediatrician to release the baby home.

Your baby now weighs about 1.9kg (4.2lb), almost the same as a pineapple, and measures over 43.7cm (17.2in) from head (crown) to heel. Your baby's brain develops rapidly throughout the third trimester. But once it is born, and all senses are stimulated, your baby's brain growth will be super-charged.

Week 34: Your bambino has thick skin! Talk about what personal items your partner wants in her overnight bag, and double-check that everything is in the suitcase. Don't forget snacks and your phone charger — and maybe a tablet loaded with games and movies in case her labor takes a long time, and you both need distractions.

Your baby is the size of an acorn squash and weighs more than 2.1kg (4.7lb) and is about 45cm (17.7in) from head (crown) to heel. It's reassuring to know that babies born at 34 weeks, who have no other health problems, are able to thrive outside the womb (uterus). If your baby is born this week, it may need a little help in the neonatal unit, but after that will be all set to do as well as if it had arrived full-term.

Week 35: Time to say "pack up," just a month to go! Ensure there's gas in the car and that you've programmed the various routes to the hospital or birthing center on your phone. It's not a bad idea to do a trial run, either, given the unpredictability of traffic flow or pop-up construction crews.

Your baby now weighs nearly 2.4kg (5.3lb), about the same as a honeydew melon, and measures around 46.2cm (18.2in) from head (crown) to heel and will gain about 30g a day over the next few weeks. It may be possible to know how your baby's moving just by looking at your partner's baby bump. Depending on the position, you may see a rise and fall as the baby rolls over, or rhythmic twitches as it gets the hiccups. Now that it's getting big, your baby's movements may feel a bit uncomfortable.

MONTH 9: WEEK 38-42

Week 36: Your baby just got cuter. If your baby decided to pop out this week, she would be considered early. So, if you haven't done so already, here is some great pregnancy advice for dads (or partners): Discuss with your boss. You might mention you need to stick close to home for the next four weeks if you travel for work.

Your baby weighs nearly 2.6kg (5.7lb) and at just over 47.4cm (18.7in), is similar in length to a romaine lettuce. The pregnancy is considered full-term by the end of this week, meaning your baby is ready to be born any day. Bear in mind, only about four percent of babies are born on their due date. Most women give birth sometime between 38 weeks and 42 weeks. Your baby's hearing is likely to take a leap in sensitivity this week. The brain and nervous system are maturing fast as your baby's arrival in the world approaches.

Week 37: Your baby is the size of a cantaloupe! Funny, that overstuffed closet never bothered you before, but now you just have to organize it. And that cabinet over there needs clearing out. Don't be surprised to suddenly find the energy (and the enthusiasm) for compulsive cleaning, painting, and organizing.

Your baby is ready for birth, and you'll be meeting your new addition in a small number of weeks. Your baby weighs over 2.9kg (6.3lb) and is about 48.6cm (19.1in) long from head (crown) to heel. Your baby continues to work their facial muscles by practicing pouts, frowns and grimaces. Their blinking and startle reflexes are more honed because their hearing has taken a leap in sensitivity.

Week 38: You now have a watermelon!!! The baby is as big as a small watermelon right now — and your partner's belly looks like one, too. You both may be in the mood, but wondering whether sex might bring on labor. If her practitioner hasn't specifically nixed the idea, then go for it. You can do the deed up to the very end.

The average weight of a baby at 38 weeks of pregnancy is about 3.1kg (6.8lb), and the average length is about 49.8cm (19.6in). The fine lanugo hair that covered your baby's body is largely gone but may still have some patches when born, particularly on the upper arms and shoulders. The baby's elbows and knees may have small dimples, and it can now make a firm grasp with its hands.

Week 39: One more week to go! To get your minds off next week's due date and take advantage before you become a family of three, seize these baby-less moments to do things you enjoy as a couple.

All of your baby's organs are well developed. The skin is becoming thicker and paler as new skin replaces the outer skin cells that are sloughing off. The baby's lungs are producing more surfactant, the substance that keeps the tiny air sacs open, and it's ready to take its first breath outside the womb (uterus).

Week 40: It's almost time! About a third of expectant women reach full term and go 40 weeks and beyond, so your partner might fall into this group. If so, stay cool and calm yourself so you can help her relax. Depending on what's going on with your partner's health, as well as the baby's status, some physicians may recommend inducing labor once the baby goes past term.

Babies born between now and 42 weeks are still considered full-term, and your midwife or doctor probably won't offer to induce your labor before 41 weeks of pregnancy.

Rest assured your baby is quite cozy where it is! Most fetal development is complete, but hair may continue to get thicker and nails may grow more too. The average newborn measures about 51.2cm (20.2in) from head (crown) to heel, and at 3.5kg (7.6lb), weighs the same as a small pumpkin. Anywhere between 5.5lb and 8.8lb is considered a normal birth weight.

Week 41: Is that baby ever coming out? Research shows that when dads support breastfeeding, 96 percent of moms are willing to give it a try (compared to 26 percent when dads aren't that into it).

Week 42: Finally, it's out! You might think your baby is overdue, but due dates are estimates and can be off by a week or two. Take advantage of this extra week to stock up on pantry-and-fridge essentials, and while you're at it, pick up essentials for your new bundle, like diapers. Once you've done all that, relax and look forward to the big day. It won't be long now.

PRETERM LABOR

Preterm labor occurs when regular contractions result in the opening of your cervix after week 20 and before week 37 of pregnancy. Preterm labor can result in premature birth. The earlier premature birth happens, the greater the health risks for your baby. Many premature babies (preemies) need special care in the neonatal intensive care unit (NICU). Preemies can also have long-term mental and physical disabilities. The specific cause of preterm labor often isn't clear. Certain risk factors might increase the chance of preterm labor, but preterm labor can also occur in pregnant women with no known risk factors.

Signs and symptoms of preterm labor include:

- Regular or frequent sensations of abdominal tightening (contractions)
- Constant low, dull backache
- A sensation of pelvic or lower abdominal pressure
- Mild abdominal cramps
- Vaginal spotting or light bleeding
- Preterm rupture of membranes — in a gush or a continuous trickle of fluid after the membrane around the baby breaks or tears
- A change in type of vaginal discharge — watery, mucus-like or bloody

Babies born before the third trimester (before 27 weeks of pregnancy) are considered periviable — or near the limit of viability. Because they're still very underdeveloped, these babies require life-saving interventions immediately after delivery and receive advanced care in a high-level NICU setting in order to survive. There, babies receive one-on-one care until they are stable enough to go to a regular pediatric unit.

WHEN TO SEE A DOCTOR

If your partner experiences any signs or symptoms of preterm labor, contact your health care provider right away. Don't worry about mistaking false labor for the real thing. Everyone will be pleased if it's a false alarm.

WHAT IS INDUCING LABOR?

Inducing labor is when your health care provider gives your partner medicine or uses other methods, like breaking her water (amniotic sac), to make labor start. The amniotic sac is the sac inside the uterus that holds the growing baby and is filled with amniotic fluid. Contractions are when the muscles of the uterus get tight and then relax. Contractions help push the baby out of the uterus.

Your provider may recommend inducing labor if mom's or the baby's health is at risk or if she's 2 weeks or more past the due date. For some women, inducing labor is the best way to keep mom and baby healthy. Inducing labor should be for medical reasons only. If there are medical reasons to induce your labor, talk to your provider about waiting until at least 39 weeks of pregnancy. This gives your baby the time it needs to grow and develop before birth.

The final trimester of pregnancy is overwhelming for the parents. They may feel anxious and desperate to get the baby out in the world ASAP, and simultaneously stressed about everything they need to prepare before the big day. It's a big milestone to achieve, with excitement levels soaring to new heights with just a few months to go. However, care should be taken by both the parents in ensuring the health and safety of both the mother and the baby since the baby has grown heavier and is at more risk of getting hurt. Your partner may need more help with everyday tasks.

6

CATCHING THE BABY! (AKA LABOR AND DELIVERY)

Many first-time fathers do not know what to expect when preparing for the birth of their child. It may seem overwhelming, intense, and complicated when thinking about the birth process. In this chapter, I'll share information and personal experience with the most delicate stage of pregnancy – labor and delivery. You'll be offered insight into the various procedures through which a child can be brought to the world, what to expect with each, as well as the benefits and associated risks with each route.

The wait is almost over, and it's time to welcome a new life, a new member of your family. You will be a dad soon, and the emotions are off the charts at the moment. This is one of the most anticipated moments of your life, and you want to make sure that everything goes as planned. To ensure the safety of your partner and your baby, it is helpful to prepare.

Both moms and dads naturally worry about the labor and delivery process. Some dads say they worry about doing the wrong thing in the delivery room, seeing their partner in pain, or being left out of important decisions. But they show up in big numbers, and most are glad that they did. Having their partners in the delivery room reduces the mom's anxiety and pain. And many dads find that meeting their baby right after birth is an experience that changes them forever—and helps them bond with their babies from those first seconds. I was one of them!

Going into delivery, I wasn't sure how I would handle it. I can be a little squeamish, but the nurse encouraged me get in there and grab one of Amy's legs! I was valuable in the process in ways I never thought I would be and I was so happy to support my wife and newborn daughter. I was up close and personal with the entire process, and I surprised myself that I was in awe the whole time and not woozy at all. It was amazing! Not all dads may handle it the same way, but you might surprise yourself – keep an open mind.

The first step to ensuring seamless labor and delivery – scratch that, it will never actually be seamless. What I *should* have said was – the first step to ensuring the most seamless L&D possible starts with a strategic plan. And a strategic backup plan. Later in this chapter, we'll get into a little more detail about creating a plan that will work for you and your partner.

Now, more than ever, support systems are vital. Parents who seek and accept support are less stressed and more relaxed. Don't be nervous...many people like being asked for help – it makes them feel they're special to you. Giving others support is a great way of creating a supportive community. When you offer or ask for help, others feel they can ask you for help in return.

TYPES OF SUPPORT

Practical support can help soothe the realities of parenting and functioning as a family. Examples of this kind of support include money, babysitters, help in emergencies, assistance with transport, help with household tasks (and pet care), and people to have fun with.

Personal support is for you as a person, and you often get it from your adult friendships and relationships. The most valuable personal support comes from available people, willing to listen and share ideas and advice and talk things over in positive and non-judgmental ways.

Information support is critical for every parent. Whether you're wondering about your partner's breastfeeding, changes to her body, managing her time, or your child's latest developments, you can look to other parents and friends.

HIRING A DOULA — WHAT ARE THE BENEFITS?

The doula is a professional trained in childbirth who provides emotional, physical, and educational support to a mother who is expecting, is experiencing labor, or has recently given birth. Their purpose is to help women have a safe, memorable, and empowering birthing experience. Most commonly, doulas attend the birth to offer support and comfort.

My wife and I used a doula and we loved having that incredible personalized resource at our disposal 24/7. Some people use a single doula and they love it. We used a doula group that had a daily on-call doula which we loved. We communicated often to talk to as many of them as we could since we didn't know which one would end up with us at the birth.

WHAT IS A MIDWIFE? WHAT ARE THE BENEFITS?

You probably know that some women opt for a midwife instead of an ob-gyn, but you might not realize why. Many women tend to think of midwives as supporting roles in the pregnancy and childbirth experience, similar to doulas or lactation consultants. But a midwife is a professional trained specifically in assisting women with every aspect of pregnancy, from prenatal care to delivery.

HOW TO FIND A MIDWIFE

Start with a Google Search. Google is your best friend when it comes to connecting to the services you want- you already know that! Most modern birth practices are easily found through a search engine. Start with the simplest, clearest terms you want, such as, "Home birth (or hospital birth or birthing center) midwife in my area". That will link you to the websites that most closely match what you want.

Next, set up consultations and listen to your instincts! Set up a consult with the midwives you and your partner feel most attracted to. Some people will meet with a few practices, others will only meet with the practice they feel most connected to from their online resources. The consult is really your time to figure out what you both want to know.

HOMEBIRTH VS. HOSPITAL DELIVERIES — PROS & CONS

Setting up the proper birth environment should be the top priority. *www.mothermag.com* shares the following pros and cons for both homebirths and hospital deliveries that new parents should keep in mind.

HOME BIRTH

Pros:

- Labor and deliver in the comfort of your own home.
- No restrictions on how many family members or friends can be present.
- Eat or drink as you wish before delivery.
- Walk around freely without monitors or IVs.

- Natural birth without intervention.
- Choose the delivery position that's works best.
- Little to no time constraints for labor and delivery.
- Avoid unnecessary medical interventions common in hospital births.
- Low risk of outside exposure to viruses or bacteria.
- Rest in your bed with your baby after delivery.
- In-home follow-up care and lactation support available.
- Undisturbed by doctors or nurses throughout the night.
- Less expensive delivery costs.

Cons:

- Most insurance policies will not cover homebirth expenses.
- Little pain relief or epidural available if birthing at home.
- Birth is messy.
- Potential risks if your midwife or caregiver is unsure of what to do in an emergency.

- May need to be transported to the hospital if complications arise and there will be a delay in your baby receiving care while in transit to the nearest hospital.
- Higher risk of injury or death if immediate care is needed.
- Responsible for recording your partner's and baby's vitals throughout the day and night, postpartum.
- Arrange for postpartum care.
- File your infant's birth certificate.

Hospital Birth

Pros:

- All access to a hospital bed with fetal monitoring, IVs, and a transducer to measure contractions to ensure everything runs smoothly from start to finish.
- Pain medication is available for those who desire assistance through delivery, and she will probably need to opt for a hospital birth if she wants an epidural.
- Support from trained nurses to help care for your baby.

- On-site lactation help.
- Hospitals supply formula for the baby during the hospital stay and enough for the first few days after returning home.
- Immediate medical assistance in emergency situations with the most advanced technology.

Cons:

- Food and fluid intake will likely be limited.
- Time limit on how long they will allow a woman to labor before using an intervention.
- Higher C-section rate than home births.
- If intervention is determined, doctors may administer Pitocin (a medication to speed up contractions), which some view as "rushing" the body's natural process.
- High hospital costs if uninsured. (Side note: if you are uninsured, now is a good time to look into health insurance.)

ADDITIONALLY, BIRTH CENTERS MAY BE AN OPTION...

WHAT IS A BIRTH CENTER?

The birth center is a health care facility for childbirth where care is provided in the midwifery and wellness model. The birth center is freestanding and not a hospital and is an integrated part of the health care system and are guided by principles of prevention, sensitivity, safety, appropriate medical intervention and cost-effectiveness. The birth center respects and facilitates a woman's right to make informed choices about her health care and her baby's health care based on her values and beliefs. The woman's family, as she defines it, is welcome to participate in the pregnancy, birth, and the postpartum period.

In the end, Amy and I were most comfortable with a traditional hospital birth. While some women have concerns about the lack of comfort or control in a hospital setting, we found that our hospital followed many of the practices we wanted, such as immediate skin-to-skin contact between baby and mom. Your options may depend on factors like where you live and your financial means. Rest assured that a safe, positive birth experience is possible in a range of settings.

UNDERGOING LABOR AND GIVING BIRTH

As a partner to a woman in labor, your biggest role is to provide support and encouragement during the entire childbirth process. The best way to do that is to know what to expect, so before it's go time, make sure you understand three things:

1. The stages of labor
2. How to time contractions and when to head to the hospital
3. Synergy between you and your partner in understanding and implementing the birth plan

In the delivery room, you're mom's advocate and her main source of comfort. Stay calm, confident, and supportive. Your partner is going to be looking to you for comfort, strength, and encouragement during the entire labor and delivery process. And though you may find it hard to watch her in pain, you'll likely discover that childbirth can be one of life's most powerful and rewarding moments.

John's story (father of twins)

During my wife's labor, my chief thinking was making sure that first, she didn't die and second, my sons didn't die. But she came first. I guess this fits the role I have always felt, being the first and last line of protection. For me, childbirth was one of those moments when I stood between my family and the universe, knowing I might be powerless to do anything, but ready just in case. This was my first thought and fear when my wife told me she was pregnant, and it stayed with me every day until the birth.

Despite this fear, I stayed surprisingly calm through the birth, although my wife was exhausted and losing blood. Her growing paleness was my number one thought, but our medical team reassured us throughout the process. In those moments I knew that no matter what happened, I would always be grateful that I was by her side.

When my boys came out, they both did the same thing, which I will always recall clearly. Twice the nurse held a boy up to me, and twice his eyes were open wider than I thought possible, looking straight into mine. They seemed very ready to take it all in, and I felt that we immediately knew each other in some kind of cosmic and primitive way.

THE STAGES OF LABOR

LABOR AND DELIVERY IS DIVIDED INTO THREE STAGES:

Labor, Pushing and birth, and Delivery of the placenta. Every woman's labor is different. And your partner's labor may be different each time she has a baby. But there are patterns to labor that are true for most women. Learning about the stages of labor and what happens during each one can help you and your partner know what to expect once labor begins.

Labor is the longest stage. For first-time moms, it can last from 12 to 19 hours. It may be shorter (about 14 hours) for moms who've already had children. Labor has started when contractions become strong and regular enough to cause the cervix to dilate (open) and thin out (efface). This lets your baby move lower into the pelvis and into the birth canal (vagina). Labor is divided into three parts: early labor, active labor and transition.

Early labor: For most first-time moms, early labor lasts about 6 to 12 hours. You can spend this time at home or wherever you're most comfortable. During early labor, she may feel mild contractions that come every 5 to 15 minutes and last 60 to 90 seconds. She may have a bloody show. This is a pink, red or bloody vaginal discharge. If your partner has heavy bleeding or bleeding like her period, call your provider right away.

Active labor: This is when you and your partner head to the hospital! Active labor usually lasts about 4 to 8 hours. It starts when contractions are regular and the cervix has dilated to 6 centimeters. In active labor, Mom's contractions get stronger, longer and more painful. You'll notice that she can no longer talk or pay attention to her surroundings during a contraction; she's using all her focus to get through it. Many women make low, loud vocalizations to manage through the pain. At this point, Amy did NOT appreciate words of encouragement during contractions. I quickly learned to provide support silently. Each contraction lasts about 45 seconds and they can be as close as 3 minutes apart. She may feel pain and pressure in her lower back. The cervix will dilate up to 10 centimeters, and the water may break at this time.

Transition: This can be the toughest and most painful part of labor. It can last 15 minutes to an hour. During transition, contractions come closer together and can last 60 to 90 seconds. Your partner may feel like she wants to bear down, feeling a lot of pressure in the lower back and rectum, and she may feel shaky and panicky.

WHAT HAPPENS IN THE SECOND STAGE OF LABOR AND DELIVERY?

In the second stage, your partner's cervix is fully dilated and ready for childbirth. This stage is the most work for her because your provider wants your partner to start pushing the baby out. This stage can be as short as 20 minutes or as long as a few hours. It may be longer for first-time moms or if she's had an epidural.

During the second stage of labor, contractions may slow down to come every 2 to 5 minutes apart. They last about 60 to 90 seconds. The baby's head begins to show. This is called crowning and your provider guides the baby out of the birth canal, possibly using special tools, like forceps or suction, to help the baby out. Then the baby is born, and the umbilical cord is cut.

WHAT HAPPENS IN THE THIRD STAGE OF LABOR AND DELIVERY?

In the third stage, the placenta is delivered. This stage is the shortest and usually doesn't take more than 20 minutes. Your partner will have contractions that are closer together and not as painful as earlier. These contractions help the placenta separate from the uterus and move into the birth canal. They begin 5 to 30 minutes after birth.

Timing Contractions: When your partner is nearing the end of her pregnancy and the due date is looming (or it has passed), it's important to start watching for signs of contractions. There are different kinds of contractions, but if you time the contractions, you'll know whether your partner is truly in labor—aka when it's time to call the midwife or head to the hospital or birth center. How to time contractions? We were taught the 5.1.1. rule – when contractions are 5 minutes apart, last for 1 minute each, and have been this way for 1 hour, it's time to go!

According to *verywellfamily.com*, there are apps for timing contractions, but the good old-fashioned way of using a watch with a second hand or a reliable digital watch works just as well. You also can use a stopwatch app on your phone. Whatever you use, here are the steps to take. Grab a notepad so you can do the simple math required to determine how long each of your contractions are lasting:

1. When a contraction begins, jot down the time.
2. When a contraction ends, write down the time.
3. Do the math: The difference between the beginning and the end of the contraction indicates how long the contraction lasted.
4. As soon as the next contraction begins, write down the time.
5. Note how much time passed from the end of the first contraction to the beginning of the second. This indicates how far apart your contractions are, or the frequency of contractions.
6. Continue timing each contraction for a few more rounds to see if they've fallen into a regular pattern yet. If they haven't, take a break.

WHY IT'S GOOD TO BE PREPARED

Going with your partner to birth classes and reading about the different stages of labor can help you get ready. This way, you'll know what's likely to help at each stage. It will also help you understand how early labor progresses so you don't rush your partner to the hospital too soon (if that's where your baby will be born).

Some men find it helps to watch births – for example, on YouTube or TV. Others visit a birthing room to have a look at the equipment. You might also want to plan your route to the hospital or the birth center, where you'll park your car if you're driving, and which entrance to go to. Don't be like my friend who accidentally parked in an entirely different section of the hospital, so his wife had to walk across two parking lots during labor!

BIRTHING CLASSES

By participating in birthing classes, men receive the encouragement and information to become better equipped for the childbirth process.

HOW ONLINE CLASSES DIFFER FROM IN-PERSON CLASSES

An online childbirth class is a great idea for some families, but an in-person class may be preferred.

Online

- Schedule flexibility
- Only option if there are no live classes near you or you are on bedrest
- You can go in-depth into a specific topic you need

In-Person

- Meeting other expectant parents
- Hands-on demonstrations
- Can ask instructor questions

Classes that are held online may or may not offer a community to talk to other people who are expecting at about the same time as you and your partner are. Many people taking a childbirth class really enjoy and learn a lot from other class participants. This is one of the biggest differences. The other being the length of the course.

Online classes, while they may cover similar topics, may be designed to go very quickly. While you and your partner do have control over how quickly you take the course, and an online course may need to build in some breaks to allow you both to process and act upon the information that you both have learned.

- **Gain confidence:** Many dads-to-be go into the birth experience lacking confidence in their ability to participate because there are so many unknowns successfully.
- **Ease fears:** Women aren't the only ones with fears about childbirth. Men have fears, too, but may not express their fears as easily — or at all.
- **Be better prepared:** Birthing classes equip couples with critical information about childbirth, including natural birth options, designing a birth plan, the power of a woman's body, and how men can best support their partners during birth.
- **Bond as a couple:** Attending birthing classes with your partner is a powerful way to show that she's not in this alone. The hour out of the week we set aside to learn about birth together built excitement and helped us feel like partners.

The most helpful thing I learned in birthing classes was how to support Amy during labor with the double hip squeeze. I grasped her hips from behind and really squeezed to help relieve some of her pelvic pressure during contractions – what a difference it made! Don't be afraid to just get right in there, dads!

BIRTH PLANS

No matter how many baby-book checklists you check your way through, how much advice you earnestly absorb from your friends with kids, or how many perfect new parent gifts you receive, no new parent ever feels "ready." When creating a plan for the arrival of your child, collaborate on solutions to all contingencies with your partner.

There is a lot to consider about birth itself. Will your baby be born in a hospital, birth center, or birthing room? Who will be present? What role will you play? Attending childbirth classes together does a lot to help answer your questions and feel more prepared for the big day.

MAKE YOUR CONTACT LIST:

Be the social media and communications butterfly for your partner, texting, tweeting and bragging about the big news when baby makes his debut. Make plans now...discuss with your partner to determine who is on the call list and in what priority. If your partner is big on sharing her story on Facebook or Instagram or another platform, ask her if she'd like to memorialize this moment, making it "Facebook Official," as they say. Make the plan together and share the joy of sharing the joy.

WHO SHOULD BE IN THE ROOM?

Your partner should be ultimately in charge of who's in the room with her at this time. Some women like to have just the significant other and the medical team; others want their mom or best friends there for support. Discuss this with her beforehand to make sure everyone is prepared for the moment.

PAIN RELIEF PREFERENCES?

The amount of pain felt during labor and delivery is different for every woman. The level of pain depends on many factors, including the size and position of the baby, the woman's level of comfort with the process, and the strength of her contractions. There are two general ways to relieve pain during labor and delivery: using medications and using natural methods (no medications). Some women choose one way, while other women rely on a combination of the two.

WHAT MEDICAL INTERVENTIONS WOULD YOU WANT TO AVOID IF POSSIBLE?

An 'intervention' is an action taken by a midwife or doctor that literally means that they intervene in the birthing process to assist in the delivery of your baby. There are several ways an intervention can occur. According to pregnancybirthbaby.org, the most common are assisted delivery by forceps or a vacuum (ventouse) cup, an episiotomy or an induced labor.

Whatever the method used, an intervention occurs when it becomes clear that your partner will be unable to give birth without some kind of assistance or the baby is in distress and needs to be born more quickly. Your baby's heart rate will be monitored throughout the labor process to watch for any signs that the baby is in distress and that something needs to be done. You and your partner should discuss all of these methods with your midwife or doctor during the pregnancy so you can both understand why they might be considered. If your partner is healthy and the pregnancy and labor are normal, she probably won't need any intervention.

PACKING FOR THE HOSPITAL

Chances are, you've both spent the past several months in anticipation of the day you and your partner finally get to meet the baby. But don't forget one of the most important third-trimester to-dos: Deciding what to pack in your hospital bag—for baby, you, and your partner. So, where to start?

Essential items and documents:

- A picture ID (driver's license or other ID)
- Your partner's insurance card
- The name and phone number of your baby's doctor **(reminder – you or your partner should contact a pediatrician several months before the due date)**.
- Your partner's **birth plan**, if you have one. (Bring extras in your hospital bag so everyone on your medical team can have a copy.)

- Cell phone and charger.
- A cord blood kit if mom plans to bank or donate your baby's cord blood.
- A safely installed, rear-facing infant car seat

Personal items:

- **Toiletries.** Pack a toothbrush and toothpaste, lip balm, deodorant, a brush and comb, makeup (if she's planning to use it), and hair ties. Dry shampoo is also a good idea.
- Sanitary pads
- Eyeglasses and contacts

Clothing for her:

- A loose bathrobe
- A nightgown or two
- Slippers and socks.
- A comfortable outfit or two
- Several pairs of postpartum underwear
- Comfortable nursing bras

Essentials for labor:

- **Comfort items.** A picture of someone or something she loves, essential oils - peppermint oil can help with nausea, and lavender to promote calm, or anything else she finds comforting. Some women even like to post an encouraging phrase or mantra to the wall.
- Massage lotion or oil (back labor is a thing!)
- Music – put your DJ Dad skills to use with a soothing set
- Books, magazines, and a tablet
- Softer lighting to create a more soothing atmosphere – such as battery tea lights, fairy lights – even a lamp from home if it's easy to pack
- Water bottles, Gatorade and a bendy straw to help her sip while she moves through positions. Labor is just that, and it's thirsty work!

Supplies for after labor:

- Snacks!
- Eye mask and earplugs
- A notepad or journal and pen. You can track your baby's feeding sessions, write down

questions for your provider, or journal about your baby's birth. Some parents bring a baby book to record the birth details right away.

- Nursing pillow. A specially designed pillow can provide better support than hospital pillows.
- Clothes for the new baby – You'll need an outfit to bring baby home in! Pack one newborn-size and one 0-3 months size since you won't know which will fit until he arrives.
- Gifts for older siblings

Remember...this isn't the time for procrastination! Make sure the bags are packed and ready to go several weeks prior to the due date. You never know when baby is on the way! In the bag ensure your partner not only has all the necessities mentioned above, but maybe a surprise treat, like new slippers or a fluffy soft robe to make her comfortable.

GETTING TO THE HOSPITAL OR BIRTH CENTER

- Map out the directions well in advance.

- Know the directions to alternate emergency facilities.
- Run the route at various times in the day and night so that you will know of any potential obstacles to getting her there on time.

Planning for Homecoming

On some level, you may have been waiting for the pregnancy to end and life to get back to normal. For the first time, you might be realizing what it means for your life to have changed. Go with the flow, and trust you will fall into a rhythm that works. It takes time to work out what your "new normal" is. Don't expect to hit your stride right out of the gate — it'll take plenty of time and practice.

It's a good idea to plan practical and emotional 'backup' after your baby is born. You don't have to do everything if others are willing to lend a hand. If you have time in the weeks before the birth, it's also a good idea to stock your freezer with nutritious meals (that is exactly what we did and it was a huge help). In the early weeks with your baby, frozen meals will be handy when you need a healthy dinner in a hurry.

. . .

Support your Partner During Birth

Giving birth can get pretty ugly. Your partner may even have a bowel movement as she's pushing and emit primal noises you've never heard before. Your job, no matter how unsettled you may feel, is to say this: "You're doing great!" Actually, she probably won't even be paying attention to your words. It's your familiar voice and reassuring tone that she'll notice. Being a birth support partner can be exhausting so look after yourself as well as her, including taking rest breaks when it works for your partner or if there is another support person there.

Basically, you are your partner's rock, offering non-stop emotional and physical support, encouragement and reassurance while guiding her through breathing and relaxation techniques. Lean on techniques you learned in pregnancy and birth classes, like offering essential oils to help with nausea or using hands-on comfort measures like the double-hip squeeze.

You are your partner's spokesperson, speaking up and ensuring she gets what she needs. If she's in the middle of a contraction or getting very tired, she might not be able to speak for herself. If you find yourself in this situation, try to stay calm and polite when you're talking to staff – they're doing their best to look after your partner and you.

For example, if your doctor or midwife suggests an unplanned medical procedure or pain medication, ask for information and time to discuss it with your partner, unless it's an emergency.

Phillip, a father of two, recounts his moments in the delivering room with his wife. He says, "I had pain where she had pain – I was trying to control it. She was moaning and she said, 'Massage me there'. I massaged there and she said, 'Don't do that!' You just have to be there in every possible capacity and that's the joy of it, because in a sense you lose yourself to it."

EPISIOTOMY: WHAT YOU NEED TO KNOW?

According to Healthline.com, the term episiotomy refers to the intentional incision of the vaginal opening to hasten delivery or avoid or decrease potential tearing.

For years, an episiotomy was thought to help prevent more extensive vaginal tears during childbirth — and heal better than a natural tear. The procedure was also thought to help preserve the muscular and connective tissue support of the pelvic floor. Today, however, research suggests that routine episiotomies don't prevent these problems after all. Routine episiotomies are no longer recommended. Still, the procedure is sometimes needed. Your health care provider might recommend an episiotomy if your baby needs to be quickly delivered because:

- Prolonged second stage of labor
- Fetal distress
- Vaginal delivery requires assistance with the use of forceps or a vacuum extractor.
- Baby in a breech presentation
- Twin or multiple deliveries
- Large-sized baby
- Abnormal position of the baby's head
- History of pelvic surgery

CERVIX DILATION

The cervix, which is the lowest portion of the uterus, stays firmly closed throughout pregnancy to protect the baby. This is why it's totally fine to have sex throughout pregnancy. The cervix begins to open when it's time to have the baby, through a process called cervical dilation. Dilation is the opening of the cervix, which is measured in centimeters (although the doctor or midwife's fingers actually do the measuring). Once she dilates to 10 centimeters (cm), she's ready to deliver the baby.

What can you do about cervical dilation? Not a thing: Your partner's body is in charge here. Once your doctor gives you that estimate for baby's arrival, just keep an eye out for signs of labor so you'll be prepared when it's time to take the mom-to-be to the hospital. She may experience a "bloody show" and, while not very common outside of movies, her water may break at the beginning of labor. Call your doctor or midwife if this happens. Remember the 5:1:1 rule: strong and regular contractions that are 5 minutes apart and last 1 minute each for 1 hour indicate that it's time to head to your hospital or birth center.

C-SECTION: WHAT, WHY, AND WHEN?

What is a C-section? A cesarean delivery — also known as a C-section or cesarean section — is a surgical delivery. It involves one incision in the mother's abdomen and another in the uterus. Your partner may need a c-section because of complications that make vaginal birth unsafe for your partner or your baby.

COMPLICATIONS DURING PREGNANCY THAT MIGHT INDICATE A C-SECTION:

- Previous C-section or other surgeries on the uterus.
- Problems with the placenta
- Infection, like HIV or genital herpes
- Medical conditions like diabetes or high blood pressure
- Multiples

COMPLICATIONS THAT AFFECT YOUR BABY OR LABOR AND BIRTH:

- Labor doesn't progress.
- The baby is very large.
- The baby isn't in a head-down position for birth. (Our baby was breech all the way up to the final weeks when she turned herself around.)

- The umbilical cord is pinched, or has an umbilical cord prolapse. (The cord was wrapped around our daughter's neck!)
- The baby is in distress.
- The baby has certain congenital birth defects.

What happens during C-section?

According to the American Pregnancy Association, the C-section can be quite simple, especially if it's a planned surgery. The doctor will make an incision in the abdomen wall first. The most common incision is made horizontally (often called a bikini cut), just above the pubic bone. The muscles of the stomach are not cut, but they will be pulled apart so that the health care provider can gain access to the uterus.

An incision will then be made into the uterus, horizontally or vertically. The health care provider will then suction out the amniotic fluid and deliver the baby through the incisions. The baby's head will be delivered first so that the mouth and nose can be cleaned out to allow it to breathe. Once the whole body is delivered, the health care provider will lift and show you your baby. The uterus will be closed with stitches that will dissolve in the body. Stitches or staples are used to close your abdominal skin.

Possible Complications of C-section:

- Bleeding / blood clots
- Breathing problems for the child
- Increased risks for future pregnancies
- Infection
- Injury to the child during surgery
- Longer recovery time compared with vaginal birth
- Surgical injury to other organs
- Adhesions, hernia, and other complications of abdominal surgery

Remember, there are risks to every type of birth – and by and large, C-sections are extremely safe.

Elective C-section

Scheduled surgery for nonmedical reasons is called an elective cesarean delivery, and your doctor may allow this option. Some women prefer to deliver by surgery because it gives them more control in deciding when their baby is born. It can also reduce some anxiety about waiting for labor to start. Some of the pros and cons of an elective C-section, according to Healthline.com, are:

Pros:

- Lower risk of incontinence and sexual dysfunction
- Lower risk of the baby being deprived of oxygen
- Lower risk of the baby experiencing trauma

Cons:

- May need a repeat cesarean delivery with future pregnancies
- Higher risk of complications with cesarean deliveries
- Longer hospital stay and a longer recovery period

WHEN DO YOU GET A DISCHARGE AFTER C-SECTION? WHAT IS THE TYPICAL RECOVERY TIME?

DURING A CESAREAN

- During a C-section your partner may feel pressure, but should not feel pain. However, the experience can be frightening especially if it was not planned. First and foremost, provide genuine comfort and praise, holding her hand, offering reassurance, helping her to understand what is happening, and keep the focus on the fact that you'll meet your baby in a few moments.

- Make sure you have a chair available, because you may just pass out! Don't worry, that's normal. When you're allowed in for the C-section, you'll be given a seat right near your wife's head. Although you may not be able to see much because a sterile drape is placed between your partner's head and the rest of her body, the whole experience may make your head spin.

- It's possible that your partner's hands and arms may be occupied during the procedure with her IV and monitoring equipment, so be ready to be the first to snuggle your little one. Make sure your partner sees the baby as soon as possible and encourage skin-to-skin

contact, which is so important for baby
and mom.

Post-Op care for mom and baby

- After a C-section birth, the average hospital
  stay is two to four days. Women who
  experience any complications during or after
  delivery may need to stay longer. Just like
  with any surgery, her body needs time to heal
  afterward.
- A C-section is major surgery, and your
  partner will need some extra TLC after, since
  it can take up to two months for some
  women to recover. Already have a plan
  mapped out for help for her during these
  tough times.

An Insight into VBAC

What is a VBAC? People who have had a cesarean
birth can usually try vaginal birth next time around
safely. This is commonly called vaginal birth after
cesarean or VBAC.

Considering VBAC: If you want to try a VBAC, it's a good idea to choose a doctor or midwife who'll support your choice.

Pros:

- Quicker recovery
- Shorter hospital stays
- Less likely to return to the hospital
- Less need for strong pain relief after birth
- More likely to touch and cuddle their babies
- Better chance of starting and continuing to breastfeed
- Less likely to have complications in future pregnancies
- More physically able to care for their babies

Cons:

- Your baby's heartbeat will be monitored more closely during labor. You might need to wear special equipment for this.
- Slightly more risk of the scar in your uterus tearing or rupturing during labor.
- Tearing

- Higher likelihood of unplanned (emergency) cesarean.

What are the odds? If a mother has had a vaginal birth before and has a healthy, uncomplicated pregnancy, this improves the chances of successful VBAC.

Birth centers, homebirth, and VBAC: It's important to discuss the options with your partner, midwife, and doctor.

NATURAL VS. EPIDURAL: WHAT IS WHAT?

According to Healthpartners.com, there's no such thing as an "unnatural birth." So, when people refer to a "natural birth," they're often referring specifically to giving birth with the use of little-to-no pain medication, giving birth at the body's pace. Advocates of "natural birth" feel that it gives the most control to women while avoiding any risks associated with pain medication.

On the other hand, there is an opportunity for an epidural to help your partner through the birthing process. An epidural block, as it's sometimes called, is an injection of anesthesia in the lower back that numbs the nerves from the waist down.

THE PROS AND CONS OF NATURAL BIRTHS

Pros:

- Fewer side effects for your partner and your baby.
- A strong feeling of control, empowerment, and accomplishment.
- The ability to change birthing positions
- The potential for quicker labor, delivery, and recovery

Cons:

- No pain medication - The pain could take away from the overall birth experience – As magical as childbirth is, pain is powerful.
- A longer labor

THE PROS AND CONS OF EPIDURALS

Pros:

- Flexible pain relief
- Non-drowsy pain relief
- With relief from the pain, she may be able to rest and recover a bit before the pushing stage

Cons:

- Headaches or nausea.
- Limited mobility
- Potential to prolong labor and reduced sensation can make pushing more difficult
- Lowered blood pressure

While an epidural is the most popular form of pain relief during labor, opioids or nitrous oxide may be options. Neither of these will provide as much relief as an epidural, but you may want to ask your medical provider about them. Because an epidural can prolong labor (and who wants that?) some women use these tools in order to wait as long as possible or even avoid an epidural.

When we made our birth plan, Amy was on the fence about wanting the epidural as she was concerned that it would slow down her progress. Luckily, her labor progressed quickly for a first-time mom. We had been up all night, and getting an epidural allowed us both to take a quick nap before gearing up to push.

Finally, the moment has arrived that you have been waiting for! The baby is now on its way and will be out in the world any second. But it's not the time to celebrate yet. You'll need to support and advocate for your partner during birth, doing your part to ensure your baby arrives safe and healthy. Reach out to your support system so you have help with pet care etc. on standby, and familiarize yourself with the signs of labor. Of course, at the end of the day, it is your partner's choice whether to use pain medications and what type of birth to have. But just know...all birth is natural, and the birth plan simply serves as a guideline during this time.

7

TAKING CARE OF THE FAMILY ECONOMY

As a father, you and your partner are entrusted with the responsibility of your children and yourselves. Everyone thinks about the enormous cost of having a child, but this is like eating an elephant – impossible to do all at once, but doable one bite at a time. If you do your math right and plan ahead, you are more than capable of meeting these challenges.

When it comes to providing financially for your little one, it's easy to feel overwhelmed. Speak to a financial adviser before taking any drastic action. Often new parents will have their eyes on a spacious new home to accommodate their growing family, but it's important to be realistic. If an upgrade means straining your budget, then you'll want to think very carefully and never compromise stability for space. As our OB told us, a baby will be happy in a dresser drawer, and more space may not be needed until your child grows older.

To make the transition a little easier, you should start by re-evaluating your household budget and determining what extra items may be needed. And it's not just clothes and diapers you'll need to consider, there's also childcare costs, healthcare costs, insurance changes and broader lifestyle changes. Be prepared to redistribute funds as well as realign long and short-term goals to accommodate the arrival of your baby.

Most modern dads want to be more than just the person who brings in the money. But it's normal to worry about whether you're a 'good enough' provider. Sometimes this worry has to do with going from two incomes to one. Or you may worry about childcare costs and stretching your time and money to make it all work.

BUDGETING FOR THE BIRTH

The arrival of a new baby can be both exciting and financially overwhelming. A tiny new baby can mean big changes and major expenses for new parents. How much money can you expect to spend on your little one in the first year? What financial tools should you consider creating? According to Investopedia.com, one of the largest expenses for new parents can be the delivery—the cost of which depends on the location and health insurance policy.

In the U.S., the average new birthing parent with insurance coverage will pay more than $4,500 for their labor and delivery, according to a 2020 research article published by the journal *Health Affairs*.

Vaginal deliveries, the researchers found, cost people an average of about $4,314 out of pocket in 2015 (up from $2,910 in 2008). The out-of-pocket cost of cesarean birth, meanwhile, went up from $3,364 to $5,161. Review your policy to find out what your out-of-pocket costs are for prenatal care, hospital stay, tests, and postpartum care.

Another large bucket of one-time costs involves setting up your home. Perhaps you and your partner are starting from scratch in many areas such as furniture, strollers, and cribs.

On top of these one-time costs, there is the potential temporary loss of income if you and/or your partner take unpaid leave. Under the Family Medical Leave Act

(FMLA), your employer may grant you and your partner up to 12 work-weeks of unpaid leave for your baby's arrival. Here again, nothing is set in stone as small businesses do not fall under the FMLA. So, check to see what type of leave you may qualify for with your employer. If you take unpaid leave, calculate your regular expenses during that period—mortgage, utilities, insurance, groceries, etc.—and determine how you will meet those costs.

BUDGETING FOR THE FIRST YEAR WITH BABY

According to WebMD, the first two years of raising a baby will run you over $25,000. The good news is it gets cheaper for every child you have. The next child can wear hand-me-downs and share a room or use an old stroller. Some things will always cost money, though. Food and diapers can't be shared. Same with medical costs and, depending on the age gap, childcare.

Many new parents buy more than what they "need." You might want a really nice rug, a really cool rocking chair, or some cute pictures to hang in the nursery. That's fine, just make sure you buy these things after creating a budget for what you actually need, like diapers. Essentials don't need to be expensive, especially things like clothes or strollers which you can find at local thrift shops or through family/friends. The cost of furnishing a nursery varies the same way the cost of furnishing your bedroom varies. Are you buying from a boutique? A thrift store? Garage sale? Get your hands on some hand-me-downs to save on costs.

To your baby, the material stuff is much less important than being cuddled and loved by you. But getting ready for baby can still be expensive. Even the basic equipment and home preparations can put a dent in the household budget. If you're feeling the strain, you could look for other options, like borrowing or hiring some equipment, or buying second-hand . We found a great bassinet that was barely used on Facebook Marketplace. One word of caution, this probably isn't the way to go for car seats. You should only buy, borrow or accept second-hand baby equipment that has the mandatory standards label and safety features. It's also a good idea to check the condition of an item physically before you buy or borrow.

According to www.incharge.org/financial-literacy, on average, families spend between $60-$200 on clothes within the first year. This varies greatly depending on your willingness to shop thrift stores and settle for hand-me-downs. Despite using less fabric, baby clothes tend to cost the same as adult ones. However, your little one will outgrow his or her onesie quickly. There's no point in being picky or stocking the closet with designer outfits. Ask friends and family members for their old baby clothes. They'll thank you for helping them free up closet space. Older cousins, if your siblings have children, are a good place to start.

Don't forget diapers & changing supplies! You've got two options here: cloth or disposable. Disposable diapers are what you're used to seeing and probably what you used to wear yourself back in the day. Cloth diapers are a cheaper and more eco-friendly option.

How about your meal budgeting for baby? When it comes to the first year of food for your baby, breastfeeding will save you money and is reported to be healthier for your baby. According to the U.S Surgeon General, breastfeeding not only protects against illnesses like pneumonia, diarrhea, and asthma, it also can save you between $1,200-$1,500 a year on formula.

Parenthood is unpredictable, at best. You can save a lot of money by not assuming that things are going to go exactly as planned. Just ask any mom who stocked up on precious itty-bitty newborn-sized baby clothes only to birth a baby that arrived already too big for those outfits. It happens! One of Amy's friends, 8 months pregnant and awash with nerves, purchased a full year of baby clothes for her son. Predictably, nothing fit exactly when expected, and he couldn't wear most of the clothes earlier or later because they were the wrong season!

That beautiful $100 baby-wearing contraption? Your baby might hate it. Those cute little Converse shoes? Indulge if you must but there's an excellent chance baby's just going to kick them off. Proceed with caution and prepare to pivot. Try to buy what you need when you need it, whenever possible.

GETTING YOUR FINANCIAL HOUSE IN ORDER

As soon as you and your partner find out your special news, you can start your financial nesting. www.youneedabudget.com suggests that the first thing you and your partner do (after you finish celebrating!) is to take a close look at your current, baby-free budget and see which expenses you can cut. Spend more time cooking at home instead of ordering take-out, check out baby-related books from the library instead of buying them from Amazon, and ditch any non-essential streaming services.

Consider cleaning out your closets and storage areas as part of your nesting plan, and sell any items that you no longer need. If you're up for it, now's the ideal time to pick up a side gig to stock up some savings to alleviate future financial stress.

Don't be afraid to ask for help before it's too late! Although most offers of financial help are well meant, sometimes you might feel that they come with conditions or expectations. If this sounds like your situation, you could start by deciding with your partner on exactly how and how often you're both happy for in-laws, family, friends and others to help out with money. It's OK for you and your partner to set the ground rules. This might take some time, negotiation and compromise. It can help if you and your partner come up with a response beforehand, so that you're both prepared if an offer comes your way.

If you plan on going from two incomes to one when the baby arrives, start living on one income as much as possible now and setting the rest aside. Future you is going to be so grateful that you thought of these things. Get realistic about your expenses, discover new ways to save, and start preparing for your new addition!

COMMUNICATION CHALLENGES - TALKING ABOUT MONEY WITH YOUR PARTNER

Talaat and Tai Mcneely, authors of *His & Her Money*, share that the biggest challenge couples face when it comes to their finances, especially when their family unit starts growing, is "usually a severe breakdown in communication. Whether that's communication between each other, or communication with reality."

The subject of money is just like everything else in your relationship: it all comes down to knowing how to communicate. Determining your financial compatibility can only start with one thing — a conversation. No matter at what stage you are in your relationship, it's never too late to start discussing money.

Some men have money worries even before they find out they're having a baby. The pregnancy and baby's arrival can make things even harder. Ongoing financial worries can be a burden that takes away from your peace of mind and ability to enjoy life. Talking about money with your partner might sound painful, but I promise you it doesn't have to be awkward. As corny as it sounds, it can actually bring you closer together. The secret to starting your first big money talk is to head in with the right attitude. One way to broach the subject is to ask for their advice or thoughts ... even if you don't need it.

Working to a budget is a challenge, but the rewards are worth it. If you slip off budget, just commit to it again and get back on track. Try to learn from the slip rather than being hard on yourself or your partner. Discuss and agree with your partner before the baby is born about how and when you'll accept help, and from whom. Think about what you'll say when people offer help.

HELPFUL FINANCIAL TOOLS

To ensure we cultivated and sustained an effective family budget, Amy and I took time from the very beginning to discuss finances, and we sit down on the first of every month and go through the previous month's expenses – and plan for the upcoming month – making sure that we are staying on track. There's great apps and web tools on the market that help paint a clear financial picture.

According to Parents.com and Jacqueline Gilchrist, founder of Mom Money Map, these are some of the top financial tools for new parents for 2022:

Mint (Free): Easily one of the best-known apps on the market (likely because it's been around since 2007), Mint is a top choice for parents among many finance and budgeting experts. "It's free and comprehensive," Jacqueline, tells Parents. "It links all of your financial accounts including checking accounts, credit cards, and investment accounts. It also tracks your budgeting and net worth. As an all-in-one tool, it saves parents time from having to check multiple apps and websites."

Daily Budget (Free): As practically any parent can attest, finding things that are simple to use is a huge win. This app is ideal for parents who want budgeting to be as easy as possible. This budgeting app makes it easy to adjust for these surprise costs and stay on budget.

Honeydue: This budgeting app was specifically designed for couples to help make managing money together easier, says budgeting and consumer finance expert Andrea Woroch. You can use Honeydue to see all of your accounts and transactions, track your budget, and set shared savings goals in one place.

Mvelopes: Budgeting can be overwhelming, not to mention time-consuming. Mvelopes promises you can create a spending plan in under 15 minutes. Mvelopes is perfect for busy parents who can never find the time to comb through their finances, notes Woroch. It uses the classic envelope budgeting system in which each expense is categorized into different envelopes, so you know exactly where your money is going each month.

Goodbudget (Free): Yet another budgeting app that relies on the envelope tracking system, Goodbudget divides your cash into envelopes representing each expense category like groceries and allows you to do it virtually without a physical paper envelope. You can also access the same Goodbudget account from two devices, which is handy for parents who share a budget.

FamZoo: FamZoo is a budgeting app designed specifically for families. It's both a budgeting tool as well as an educational product that teaches kids about money, and you can schedule chores and allowances and then split the payments into savings, spending, and giving accounts to demonstrate how to be responsible with money. You can even pay interest and teach your children about the value of compound interest.

It's time to start an emergency savings account

Growing your family needs to go hand-in-hand with growing your savings, and an emergency fund will be more important than ever once you have a child to provide for. As a minimum, you should aim to have enough cash in an easily accessible account to cover 3-6 months of necessary expenses. That way if the unexpected happens, and for whatever reason you find yourself unable to work, you'll at least be able to pay the bills until you get back on your feet.

Saving goals

Opening a savings account, such as a 529 for education expenses, in your newborn's name is a great gift and savings vehicle for your child as they grow. This is a state-sponsored program that lets parents, relatives, and friends invest for a child's college education. The account belongs to you, not your child, and you remain in control of the money.

You may even want to set up a personal savings account for your child and contribute to it over the years. It might seem like a long-way off, but by the time they hit their mid-20s you could have enough saved to put down a deposit on their first home or to pay for their wedding. Lending your child a helping hand is a wonderful gesture but do make sure it's not at the expense of your own long-term saving goals. In particular, you should only target these goals if you are able to do so alongside putting sufficient funds into a retirement pot.

When you have a child, you'll want them to have experiences they will recall and savor throughout life. It's true some of the best experiences are free but sometimes it's worth spending money on family memories. And it doesn't have to be a big blow-out either! You could save up for things like music lessons, a visit to the theatre or a family holiday (even just a staycation). It's the experiences you share with your family that bring you closer together so don't forget to save for the good times too. Amy and I set up separate savings accounts for things like home repairs, family vacation/experiences, and a new car fund.

There are so many tools available to help save money in this day and age. For example, we use the Acorns.com app which rounds up purchases to the next whole dollar amount. It deposits the "spare change" into a savings account, and we don't even notice. We have saved for a whole vacation with the Acorns.com app! Seeing our various accounts grow slowly but surely provides reassurance that we'll have what we need when we need it.

8

ENSURING YOUR AND YOUR PARTNER'S WELL-BEING

A first-time pregnancy is full of wonder, excitement, and anticipation. Will you have a boy or a girl? What about twins? How will you decorate the nursery? A first-time pregnancy is also full of constant change. Especially for the mom-to-be as her body adjusts to the new life growing inside her. With the focus naturally and rightly on Mom. Dads can sometimes feel like bystanders, just watching it all happen.

True, Pregnancy and giving birth is a life-changing phase in a woman's life. She undergoes a slew of physical and mental changes during pregnancy that put her endurance and sanity to the test. It's not uncommon for a woman to drift into depression and get stuck there. With her partner's support, her journey can become much easier.

While supporting your partner is of utmost importance, you and your health, both physical and mental, are vital. Again, remember the whole thing about putting on your oxygen mask first? In the postpartum period, it is easy to focus on mothers but you may also need support, as you have a lot to come to terms with and deal with. The support they might need can be in relation to sleep deprivation, financial worries, a change in responsibilities or changes in relationship dynamics. For both parents the arrival of a new baby brings with it enormous life changes and adjustments.

Here are five ways dads-to-be can help make life easier for their partners during a first-time pregnancy, and in doing so be an active participant in the adventure.

"What can I do to make your life easier?"

Listening carefully to her answer will provide a game plan for the months leading up to delivery. Rather than assuming you know what she wants or needs, asking for specifics helps Dad customize the task list to Mom's preference. What tasks around the house does she hate to do? Even little things can make a big difference. Bringing in the mail, gassing up her car, and running those random errands to the post office and dry cleaner allow Mom to relax a little and focus on other aspects of preparing to bring a new baby into the world.

"How can I make things safer for you?"

There are also tasks that may be unsafe for Mom to do during pregnancy—like cleaning the litter box. Why is this dangerous? Toxoplasmosis is an infection that is spread in cat feces. It can cause birth defects such as mental disabilities and serious eye problems. Scooping kitty litter is definitely a job for Dad while waiting for the baby to arrive.

"I'll be your Personal Chef!"

Some men learn to cook during their partner's first pregnancy. Assuming the role of chef can be a win-win. Dad expands his culinary skills while giving Mom a break in the kitchen. She may especially appreciate this during the first trimester when food aversions are strongest. The way food tastes and smells can change for a woman during pregnancy. Her favorite foods before getting pregnant can now make Mom feel sick. Mom might also have strong cravings for specific foods that can quickly change. Tailoring the menu to these cravings and aversions is another way Dad can help with a first-time pregnancy.

"Let me Pamper you!"

Dads have an opportunity to be the prince when they pamper the mom-to-be. There are plenty of creative ways to be her hero. Pregnancy is a tiring experience. As the baby grows and Mom's body adjusts, energy levels change and sleeping can be difficult. Buying her a pregnancy pillow can help her find a comfortable position and get the rest she needs. "Self-care" days are special anytime but are even more appreciated during pregnancy. Arranging a spa day for the mom-to-be is an excellent way for Dad to pamper her. Manicures, pedicures, massages, and facials will help Mom feel relaxed and refreshed.

"I WILL BE PATIENT!!!"

Mood swings are part of being pregnant. One big reason for pregnancy mood swings are her rapidly changing hormones—specifically estrogen and progesterone. Estrogen levels soar during the first 12 weeks of pregnancy, increasing by more than 100 times. Perhaps the best way Dad can help during a first-time pregnancy is to be steady emotional support for his partner. While most couples can laugh about it after the baby arrives, mood swings in the nine months leading up to delivery day are a real thing. Going along with the "mood du jour" and accommodating Mom's wishes when her hormones bounce back and forth is an act of kindness that will certainly be appreciated.

Pregnancy is a life-changing experience for both parents. When Dad offers his help and shows kindness in tangible ways, both Dad and Mom feel like partners in the process. This is probably the toughest period in your partner's life so far (and yours, as well!). Hence, it's your primary responsibility to take good care of your partner and be there when they need you. That said, in no way should you take yourself for granted. Achieving a balance is what you should aim for, and Whattoexpect/pregnancy.com shares just how you can start to work towards that:

Listen and talk: Ensure your partner knows she can vent to you about all those little (and big!) changes going on now. She may be nervous about an upcoming procedure, or may be concerned about being the right kind of mom. She may even be stressed out about her appearance and swollen feet. Even if you think her concerns are outsized or illogical, they aren't small to her. Listen to her and support her in locating information or just take some time to have fun together.

ENCOURAGING GOOD PHYSICAL HEALTH OF THE MOTHER

All fathers worry about their partner's health and the development of their baby during pregnancy. Fathers naturally want to protect their loved ones from harm. If you are an expectant father, you can rest assured that most women have perfectly normal pregnancies and deliveries. Also, the vast majority of babies are born healthy and without complications. Pregnancy and childbirth are natural life events that do not generally pose a physical threat to your partner, especially if they are receiving proper medical care.

There are things you can do to help your partner have a safe and comfortable pregnancy. Make sure she receives the best medical care possible. Attending medical appointments with your partner will demystify the pregnancy. Hearing your baby's heartbeat for the first time or seeing your baby swim around on an ultrasound will make the pregnancy "real" for you. Your partner will also appreciate if you go with her when she needs to have medical tests done, especially if your baby's health is compromised in any way. Another thing you can do to help is to make your partner's life as stress-free as possible. Take on some extra chores so that she can rest. Be there for her when she needs your emotional support.

Encourage your partner to eat a proper diet, get enough exercise, and stay away from alcohol and cigarettes. The best way to do this is to eat the same diet, exercise along with her, and stop drinking and smoking yourself. Try not to think of these changes as a huge sacrifice, but rather as a way to experience the pregnancy with your partner.

Now that she's eating for two (or more!), this is not the time to cut calories or go on a diet. In fact, it's just the opposite — she needs about 300 extra calories a day, especially later in the pregnancy when your baby grows quickly. If she's very thin, very active, or carrying multiples, she'll need even more. But if she's overweight (and don't YOU tell her that!!!), your health care provider may advise her to consume fewer extra calories.

Healthy eating is always important, but especially during pregnancy. So, make sure her calories come from nutritious foods that will contribute to your baby's growth and development. Try to maintain a well-balanced diet that incorporates the dietary guidelines including lean protein, fruits, vegetables, whole-grain breads, and high-quality dairy products.

By eating a healthy, balanced diet, your partner is more likely to get the nutrients she needs, but will need more of the essential nutrients (especially calcium, iron, and folate) than she did before she became pregnant. Prenatal vitamins help fill any gaps to ensure both she and your growing baby are getting enough.

EXERCISE DURING PREGNANCY

According to the March of Dimes, healthy pregnant women need at least 2½ hours of moderate-intensity aerobic activity each week. Aerobic activities make you breathe faster and deeply and make your heart beat faster. Moderate-intensity means you're active enough to sweat and increase your heart rate. Taking a brisk walk is an example of moderate-intensity aerobic activity. If she can't talk normally during an activity, she may be working too hard.

Talk to your health care provider about exercising during pregnancy. For most pregnant women, exercising is safe and healthy for you and your baby. If you and your pregnancy are healthy, exercise won't increase the risk of having a miscarriage, a premature baby (born before 37 weeks of pregnancy) or a baby born with low birthweight (less than 5 pounds, 8 ounces).

WHAT KINDS OF ACTIVITIES ARE SAFE DURING PREGNANCY?

- **Walking.** Taking a brisk walk is a great workout that doesn't strain her joints and muscles. If she's new to exercise, this is a great activity.
- **Swimming and water workouts.** The water supports the weight of the growing baby and moving against the water helps keep heart rate up. It's also easy on your joints and

muscles. If she has low back pain when you do other activities, try swimming.

- **Riding a stationary bike.** This is safer than riding a regular bicycle during pregnancy. She's less likely to fall off a stationary bike than a regular bike, even as her belly grows.

- **Yoga and Pilates classes.** The instructor can help modify or avoid poses that may be unsafe for pregnant women, such as lying on your belly or flat (after the first trimester). Some gyms and community centers offer prenatal yoga and Pilates classes just for pregnant women.

- **Low-impact aerobics classes.** During low-impact aerobics, always have one foot on the ground or equipment. Examples of low-impact aerobics include walking, riding a stationary bike and using an elliptical machine.

- **Strength training.** Strength training can help build muscle and make bones strong. It's safe to work out with weights as long as they're not too heavy.

How can I limit exposure to chemicals at home?

There are some things, like alcohol, cigarettes and illegal or recreational drugs, which contain chemicals that we know can be very harmful in pregnancy. There is clear evidence that stopping these activities is one of the best things you can do to protect your baby's health during pregnancy and after they are born. Some chemicals found in everyday household items may also be worth avoiding. These include chemicals found in cosmetic products including nail polish, moisturizers, shower gels and hairsprays, cleaning products, air fresheners, paints or glues, and chemicals used to preserve furniture. This is not the time to refinish your floors!

According to the Environmental Working Group (EWG), cosmetics are poorly regulated and commonly made from untested chemicals. The good news is that there are more and more "clean" brands on the market that cater to customers who want to minimize exposure to potentially toxic chemicals. The EWG maintains a database of personal care products with safety ratings at https://www.ewg.org/skindeep/.

When cleaning, using ingredients like vinegar, baking soda and lemon to clean is one way to avoid taking unnecessary chances. When you or your partner do use cleaning products, ventilate the room during and after cleaning by opening the windows to get some fresh air. Like with cosmetics, there are now many "clean" cleaners out there, and the EWG website is a great resource to find these options.

There is growing concern over Bisphenol-A, or BPA, a compound found in plastic food containers, such as canned goods and single-use water bottles. BPA mimics estrogen and could interfere with normal chemical signals during pregnancy. More research is needed, but it's a good idea to minimize exposure. We invested in glass Tupperware, and Amy is vigilant about not letting anyone microwave plastic in our house. Check the US Health and Human Services website (hhs.gov/safety/bpa) for more advice.

Fortunately, research shows that usual levels of exposure to chemicals found in everyday household items are low. They have not been proven to have a significant impact on a baby's development.

Another area to target is your exposure to pesticides through conventionally-grown produce and meats. Organic food can be expensive, and not all foods are created equal in terms of pesticide exposure. We rely on the EWG's "clean 15" and "dirty dozen" lists to know what conventional produce is safest, versus when it's better to buy organic if you can.

Finally, did you know that our water and dust contains traces of chemicals? Investing in a high-quality water filter as well as dusting and vacuuming regularly can also help keep your home as healthy as possible.

SUPPORTING YOUR RELATIONSHIP AND SETTING A FAMILY VISION

Have you considered what kind of parent you want to be or are you barely getting through each day and constantly questioning whether you are ready to be a father? Dr. Benjamin Carson once said "There is no job more important than parenting." And he's right. Parenting takes a lot of work. And if we're to become the parents we wish we could be, then we need to be intentional with the ways in which we want to raise our children. As with any important task or life's work, it's critical to have a vision and a plan.

Focusing first on a long-term vision provides a framework and foundation to develop short-term goals. As your vision narrows to focus on the short term, it becomes more detailed and helps you form an action plan.

A parenting vision will provide you with the framework and the means by which to gauge your progress as a parent. If you're not sure where to start, consider asking yourself these questions:

- What kind of parent do I want to be?
- What kind of parents were my parents? What do I want to emulate, and what do I want to do differently?
- What kind of parents did my partner have, and how does she want to do things similarly or differently?
- What do I consider success for myself?
- What does my partner consider success for herself?
- What do I consider success for our child?
- What does my partner consider success for our child?
- What values do I want our child to have?
- What values does my partner want our child to have?
- What are my strengths?
- What are my partner's strengths?

- What are my weaknesses/limitations?
- What are my partner's weaknesses/limitations?
- What challenges me most?
- What challenges my partner most?
- How can we overcome these challenges together?

The important thing for parents to understand is that you are not alone. Successful parents build relationships with lots of different people along the way, from family to friends and teachers. Community will make your child's future so much richer. For now, take the first step of discussing your vision with your partner; in time, it can become reality, and that cliff will seem like a stepping stone.

How to Help Mom in the First Few Weeks after Pregnancy

Bringing a baby home is such an exciting time – but it can also be a bit overwhelming as you try and find the new "normal". Often, it can be difficult to find the best ways for a new dad to help a new mom – and bond with a baby (especially when Mom is breastfeeding!) Here are some easy ways for you to be involved in a way that will help Mom out and help you bond with your new child (most of which don't involve feeding!)

When your baby is first born, it may seem like all you do is feed them and change their diaper. And, in all honesty – that is about all you do! A lot of this responsibility tends to fall on the new mom – especially if they are breastfeeding. Some well-meaning dads offer to give a bottle so mom can sleep, but in order to maintain a healthy milk supply, mom will have to pump anyway, which kind of defeats the purpose.

So often I hear mothers saying that their child's father wants so desperately to help in some way, but they just don't know what's helpful or if there's anything they can do besides feeding the baby. Or maybe they feel like they are missing out on some kind of bonding experience because they can't feed the baby. This can make any new mom feel a little bit guilty!

But the truth is – there are SO many new ways to help a new mom that doesn't involve feeding the baby. Amy and I found it was helpful when I got up with her throughout the night in the early weeks. When our daughter started crying, I would help rouse Amy from sleep and go change the baby's diaper while she prepared to breastfeed. When the feeding was finished, I re-swaddled the baby in the bassinet for another few hours of sleep. Then we would do it all over again.

As you get to know your new addition, you'll realize that there are plenty of ways to bond with a baby. The responsibility of raising your child and running a household isn't just on the mom. I think it's important for new dads to feel encouraged and know they are playing an active role in the rearing of their new child. It's a partnership – and it should work like one!

Pregnancy is one of the most challenging times in the life of women, but their partners can also be strongly affected. Paying attention to your partner's physical and emotional needs will help keep her – and the baby - healthy and your relationship strong. Key to protecting the health of your child is to get regular prenatal care. That said, the dads mustn't overlook their own well-being. A healthy relationship exists only where both the partners involved are given equal importance and care.

9

WELCOME TO THE FIRST WEEK OF FATHERHOOD!

F atherhood is one of the sweetest times of a person's life. It opens the door to strengthening the bond with their partners, besides offering valuable life lessons and teaches the value of relationships and family. Exciting as it is, fatherhood brings with it a complete package of its own challenges. Prepping for the new-fatherhood phase can help cement confidence in your ability to handle the challenges head on.

When your new baby arrives, usually, the focus is on Mom and the new baby's bond, which makes total sense! Science shows that a strong bond between a mother and child boasts lots of benefits, like increased immunity. So, just how long does it take for dad to bond with newborn baby? According to happiestbaby.com, studies show that 20% of new parents may not feel any emotional attachment to their newborn baby. It's completely natural for it to take weeks or even months to develop an emotional bond with your baby. If you're one of those parents, then don't worry. Your bond with your baby will come with time.

After assisting with the birth and seeing my daughter for the first time, I was very caught up in the moment and the tears flowed. By the time we got the baby home, I was feeling more like we were babysitting someone else's baby - I don't know if disbelief set in about having created this little miracle or what, but I can honestly say I was distraught about my feelings not meeting my expectations. I expected that I'd have all of these overwhelming feelings of devotion, indescribably love, constant awe of this amazing baby, and while I had a degree of those feelings, I wasn't anywhere near the level that I felt I'd heard other men describe.

A week or two later, Amy and I remembered that I needed to have my genetic testing done to check for any inheritable abnormalities that could cause complications. I was supposed to get this done while we were still pregnant but it just slipped through the cracks. Amy had an abnormality in her testing that could prove deadly to the baby if I had the same one.

When I got the results back, I had an abnormality and, reading quickly, I thought it matched hers, meaning that my baby was in severe danger of having a very short and painful life.

I completely lost it – I was hysterical. I immediately got on the phone with the genetic counselor, and we quickly discovered that I had misread the results. My abnormality didn't match Amy's, and the baby wasn't in any more danger than other healthy babies.

In that moment, I felt flooded with all of those feelings that I thought should have been there all along. I felt a one-ness with my daughter and a love that was beyond anything I could've imagined.

With new babies, there are two essential tasks: taking care of them and getting to know them. Looking after babies involves relatively simple skills. You need to feed them, interact with them, comfort them when they're upset, keep them reasonably clean and give them a safe, comfortable place to sleep. Mind you, the skills may not seem so simple the first time you're confronted with a little mass of waving arms and kicking legs who, upon being lowered to the change table, reaches desperately as if you had dropped him into an abyss. However, baby care is easily learned by almost anyone who is willing to (or has to) get in there and do it.

Getting in there and doing it also helps with your other task, which is getting to know him. In fact, the two are interdependent: You get to know your baby partly by handling and caring for him. At the same time, knowing him makes you more attentive, which enables you to better understand and respond to his needs. And all of this helps you bond with your baby.

I remember asking a friend once—this was before I had kids—how he knew what the baby wanted. "He tells you," my friend replied. I had no idea what he meant. How can a baby tell you? But now that I've had a little girl of my own, I understand. The baby does tell you, but not with words or gestures or even looks that pass between you. It's more that, as you spend time together, you learn to read the baby's cues—her body language or her cries or coos in various situations. Whatever you might think of your partner's apparent instinct for this, it's an acquired skill that requires time and togetherness.

Part of developing the ability to read cues involves fathers and babies becoming comfortable together. I mean physically comfortable. Again, this takes time and daily caregiving helps because changing, dressing, bathing and comforting all require you to touch the baby. But there's a particular level of physical contact that comes when parents and babies are just hanging out, and getting to this place means finding the way your bodies fit together. Quiet, relaxed time together helps you find this fit.

WHAT CAN YOU DO TO PROACTIVELY BUILD A BOND WITH YOUR NEW BUNDLE OF JOY?

Even though there's less emphasis on this relationship in the early days of a little one's life, that doesn't make it any less important. And there are a few easy ways to strengthen this special father-child relationship from day one. Here are 6 simple dad-baby bonding activities to try.

1. Learn the 5 S's: By learning the 5 S's—the key to the calming reflex—you can become the master of soothing your baby. The 5 S's are an on switch for calming and an off switch for crying. Some babies need all 5 S's (swaddling, side or stomach position, shushing, swinging, and sucking) to really settle, and some just need a few to quiet them down. As a new dad, you can help your baby to be the calmest baby on the block. That will lead to a budding relationship between father and baby, and give Mom a well-needed break. Bonus: Dads tend to be amazing baby-calmers!

2. Skin-to-skin contact: We know that skin-to-skin contact is a helpful bonding tool between Mom and baby, as it prompts the body to release hormones that relieve stress. Did you know the same thing happens when Dad has skin-to-skin contact with his little one? This is a great way to strengthen Dad's bond with baby, and it even results in less crying! Talk about a win-win.

3. Massage: You know how aah-mazing you feel after a massage? Well, babies love them, too! Give your little one a massage after bath time or before bedtime.

4. Take a walk: Hit the road with your baby in tow. Bonus points if you use a baby carrier so they're right on your chest! They'll enjoy the sights and sounds and being nice and close to you (and Mom probably won't mind the extra time to herself either).

5. Become a diaper dad to bond with baby: Take over diaper duty. If Mom chooses to breastfeed, you can't step in there, but you can make diapers your domain. If this doesn't sound like a bonding activity, think twice. You can tickle, play peek-a-boo, and sing to your little one as you change them.

6. Hanging out is a great way for dads to bond with baby: Place your baby on your lap and spend time looking into each other's eyes, giggling, and cooing. This time is so fleeting and precious. Before you know it, you'll blink and that baby on your lap will be talking and walking...and on their way to kindergarten! By taking a few minutes just to enjoy these short-lived baby days, you'll make memories that will last forever.

In the Beginning...

In the early days, dads can sometimes feel like the secondary parent. Perhaps taking a back seat and assuming that their partner has it all together when it comes to feeding, soothing and caring. In reality, while moms might have a head start with becoming a parent through pregnancy and giving birth, dads can – and do – play an important role. Here's just a few tips to get you through the first week of your new and improved job:

Don't worry...you won't break your baby!

Newborns seem so fragile at this age – with their little heads lolling all over the place. You wouldn't be the first dad to worry you might 'break' them or feel awkward picking them up. But holding them and looking after them is all part of the bonding experience. And the more you do it, the easier it'll become. Really. Finding out how your baby likes to be held and soothed will also help you feel close to them.

FAMILY AND FRIENDS

In the first week, you might be bombarded with requests from family and friends to meet your new baby. While all the attention is lovely, it can be a lot to deal with. Especially when you and your partner are likely to be feeling worn out. If that's the case, try to limit visits and enjoy this special time for your new family.

ACCEPT ALL OFFERS

This is exactly the time to accept help or ask for it. If somebody offers to do your washing or cook for you, take them up on it. When people do visit, don't feel that the normal rules of hospitality apply. Say yes if they offer to bring a meal with them. Being able to just heat up some food someone else has prepared when you're shattered and hungry is a lifesaver. Nobody will expect the house to be spotless.

HELPING YOUR PARTNER RECOVER AFTER THE BIRTH

Giving birth is physically and emotionally demanding. Regardless of the type of birth she had, you can support your partner's recovery in lots of ways. Encourage her to rest when she can and not over-do it. Staying in bed might be the best way to do this for some women. If that's the case for you, your partner will appreciate you bringing her snacks and drinks. And just generally making sure she has what she needs.

AS WELL AS PHYSICAL SUPPORT, EMOTIONAL SUPPORT IS SO IMPORTANT TOO

Tell her often that you think she's doing a great job. Right now, she's probably at her most vulnerable so it's important to know that you're with her all the way. Even if she gets moody or emotional at times, try not to let this affect you negatively. Think about your emotional needs too and seek more support from your family and friends if needed. Talking through how you're feeling can help. While emotional lows are normal, if your partner's emotions or behavior doesn't feel right, it could be a sign of postnatal depression.

LACK OF SLEEP

Everybody will have told you how exhausting the early days and weeks can be. Yet nothing can really prepare you for the lack of sleep after becoming a new dad. It might not help much to know that sleep deprivation is common among new parents but at least you know you're not alone.

Sleep can be one of the most contentious issues after having a baby, as it can feel like neither you nor your partner are getting enough sleep. Probably neither of you are. Have an honest conversation about sleep and sleeping arrangements. If your partner is getting up to look after the baby, maybe let her get some rest during the day. Or do your bit at the weekend and be the one to answer that 5am wakeup call from your little one.

FEEDING YOUR BABY

Babies like to feed frequently which is normal and healthy. This is mainly because they have such small tummies and to also help establish a good breastmilk supply. Some new dads find that if their partner is breastfeeding, they're not sure what they can do to help. But you can support your partner in a number of practical ways. You could try fetching drinks (yes, that really is important) and bringing the baby to and from your partner for feedings.

It's also important to know that breastfeeding might be difficult or painful at first, and some moms run into issues such as low milk supply. It took Amy a couple of weeks until she and my daughter figured out how to nurse comfortably. It's common for moms to feel guilty, sad, scared and frustrated as they struggle through the early days. You can help by offering words of encouragement and support, and above all a nonjudgmental listening ear.

Look after yourself

Having a baby can be all-consuming at first, but remember to put aside some time for you to do the things you used to enjoy. Don't put the rest of your life on hold indefinitely. You've got to look after your new son or daughter but you've got to make sure you have a bit of me time as well. As the days go on, plan to do some of the things you enjoy, find a way to build that in.

The early days with our daughter were a blur. We didn't realize that babies not only have no concept of day and night, but actually have their days and nights mixed up! They sort this out after a few days, especially with exposure to activity and light (windows are great) during the daytime.

SAFETY FIRST

Some important advice our doctor gave to us was: constant crying can be extremely stressful. If you ever feel completely overwhelmed, angry and scared that you could harm your child, put him down safely on a flat surface and walk into another room. He will be ok crying on his own for several minutes while you take the time to take a few deep, calming breaths.

You know how the flight attendant always says, "Put on your mask before you try to help others"? Well, the same concept goes here. Don't forget that *you* need to be healthy emotionally, psychologically, and physically before you can be effective in helping your partner.

Don't be afraid to reach out to first-time dad support groups, virtual and in person. There are countless Facebook groups for new and expecting Dads out there including one that I began called "First Time Father: A Men's Group for Dads and Dads-to-be". I love to welcome new and expecting dad's into our active community. Seek out and create connections with other new fathers. Ask trusted family members, friends, or coworkers if you have questions or just need to vent. Once *you* are alright, you can jump in and make sure your partner is happy and healthy so that you can both be effective co-parents.

When you're ready to be that supportive partner, here's a few suggestions to try. You'll be happy you did! (And so will she...and so will baby).

- Affirm her by telling her how proud you are, that she's doing a great job, and how much you love her.
- Keep her hydrated by keeping her water glass full. She'll need extra more hydration than usual to recover from labor and to support a healthy milk supply, if breastfeeding.
- Make sure that she eats enough by bringing her snacks and meals. Want extra Dad points?

Make her lactation cookies – there's many recipes online.

- Give her space to take a long bath or a shower. If the baby is upset but not hungry, take him for a walk to get some fresh air. If she doesn't hear crying, she won't be tempted to rush and will be able to relax.

- Help her process the birth. Childbirth is intense, to say the least. Talking is an important way that women process this transformative experience, especially if aspects of the birth did not go the way she wanted. Do not get annoyed by this, rather ask questions and share your memories of the experience and how amazing she was.

- Listen to her. Put down your phone, pause the TV and practice active listening, repeating the key points of what she tells you. She'll feel comforted when she feels heard.

- Do not attempt to "fix" her emotions. Remember, it will take time for her hormones to settle. Often time will solve all problems. That said, if you become concerned and suspect postpartum depression, a few valuable resources include

www.postpartum.net/ and www.
postpartumdepression.org/resources/

- Send her out to get her nails or hair done so she can connect to her pre-baby self.

- Prepare to roll with some mess – and roll up your sleeves – help tidy up if chores start to pile up. Some disarray is inevitable until you both figure out how to make the "new normal" work.

- Get up with her for nighttime feedings – change baby's diaper while she gets ready to breastfeed – or prep and feed the bottle. Being a team player makes a HUGE difference for her over long nights.

- Encourage her to buy some new clothes. After having a baby, her maternity clothes won't fit right, and neither will her pre-pregnancy clothes, which can leave Mom without much to wear. Even though this phase only lasts a short while, spending a little money to feel comfortable in clothes that fit *now* can reduce the pressure she may feel to "lose the baby weight" and is a worthwhile investment in her happiness.

- Ask yourself the question, "If I were her right now, what do I think I would need"

New Parent Sex

Be patient for the return of sexual intimacy. After an uncomplicated vaginal delivery, the recommendation is to wait at least 6 weeks. She'll need to confirm with her OB. However, even after she has physically healed, it may take much more time for her to feel "ready." Fear of pain, low libido due to breastfeeding hormones, feeling "touched out" by constant physical contact with a newborn, and body image concerns can all affect Mom's desire. It's understandable to feel rejected if your partner has no interest in sex, but it's **not** about you.

You may find that your libido is also affected. Sex may take a backseat to sleep for both of you, even for many months. It can also be hard to get "in the mood" when you have one ear open for a baby's cries! Rest assured that your sexual connection will return in due time.

When you do get things going again, take it slow and release any expectations. She may want you to handle her breasts differently – or not at all. She may experience sensations differently or be shy about her changed body. Be creative, and explore all the ways that you can be together sexually with or without intercourse.

Babies don't emerge from the womb with a how-to manual for new dads in hand. Instead, they turn your whole world upside down. The first five months of a newborn's life can be profoundly disorienting for a new dad and mom. As things are constantly changing, routines can be hard to establish, and you start to wonder whether your life will ever resemble something familiar again.

Luckily, a little advice from those who've been there can go a long way in surviving the ups and downs of being a first-time dad. In that intense first month, being a good dad to a newborn is all about working to establish routines while struggling with sleep schedules, nutritional demands, breastfeeding, and safety concerns.

Fatherhood brings in a variety of challenges. You're not only responsible to take care of your partner and your baby, but also yourself. Hence, doing some advance planning and budgeting can make things way smoother for you and your family.

CONCLUSION

Y ou've heard this before, and we'll keep saying it. Be there! When I say "be there" I don't mean "stand by." You need to actively show your child that you're always dependable, always ready to help, always caring.

If you want your child to grow up into somebody you can be proud of, he needs you to show him how. Your partner needs to know there's a guy who puts her first. Your support once the baby arrives is what she will remember in the years ahead.

Help yourself and your child by eating right, getting enough sleep, exercise, and staying away from illicit drugs and excessive alcohol consumption. Leave time for you. Believe it or not, to be a good dad, you will need to have time for yourself, doing things you enjoy that you can't do with your baby or partner. Things like going out with your buddies, playing music or video games, working out or reading. It's healthy for you to get out sometimes. You get a chance to relax and think about other things. Then you're fresh and ready to do the "baby thing" when you come back. It may be hard to imagine taking time for yourself in the early newborn days, but over time you will find a rhythm and be able to regularly take some time just for you. There's time for friends and time for being a dad.

You will make mistakes along the way, but no matter how imperfect we are, your child needs *you*! Little can compare to a child's love, to your baby falling asleep in your arms, comforting a child scared by a nightmare or seeing your child's delight over knocking down a sand castle. Whatever happens along the way, a dad can always be special to his child.

Being a great first-time father doesn't mean being perfect; it means participating in the experience with empathy and confidence. From the basics of pregnancy, to designing a birthing plan, to tips on being helpful and supportive for your partner, we hope that *First Time Father* has provided you with a head start to become a fully prepared parent:

. . .

Focus on one month at a time

Reference the first few chapters to know what to expect and which milestones are coming up in each trimester:

- The first trimester: 0–12 weeks
- The second trimester: 13–27 weeks
- The third trimester: 28–40 weeks

Look forward to your growing family

Bond as a couple – and future co-parents – by setting family goals, creating a fun pregnancy announcement or planning a relaxing trip.

Support your partner

Communication is key. Doing extra housework, cooking delicious treats, and doing the legwork to prepare for your new baby doesn't hurt either!

But wait! You've not only learned how to help your partner through this amazing, scary, exhausting, exciting, and memorable time, but you've also gleaned just how to help YOURSELF get through this crazy roller coaster! Here's a recap of the most important tips to keep yourself healthy (so you can keep your partner healthy!):

TAKE TIME FOR YOURSELF!

Make sure you spend time doing some of your favorite things (especially if this is your first baby). Pay close attention to your pregnant partner's needs but don't neglect yours along the way.

GET INVOLVED!

You're the dad so play an active part in the pregnancy. Help your partner feel supported and your baby get a good start in life. Don't look back and wish you had been there.

DON'T FORGET YOU'RE IMPORTANT TOO!

Mom may be getting all the attention, but remember that there wouldn't be any baby without you. Set an example by being there during the pregnancy and delivery. You'll have a big role in the future as the father of this baby — start things off right during pregnancy.

MAKE MONEY MOVES.

Get financially fit. Prepare by budgeting now for added expenses, from one-time costs like hospital fees, to ongoing expenses like diapers. Talk early and often with your partner about finances and use apps to track spending.

DISCOVER WAYS TO GET HEALTHIER!

Are you a smoker? This is the best time to change that habit. Do you eat too much fast food? Find healthier foods to eat. Your health is important, and it'll help you keep good choices in mind when it comes to your child.

AND NOW THAT YOU'RE HEALTHY, YOU CAN HIT THE GROUND RUNNING AS...A FIRST-TIME FATHER!

It may take you some time to "feel" like Dad and bond with your new arrival. Pitch in where you can – diaper duty, anyone? – and you'll soon discover all the reasons you and this little human were meant to be together.

You and your partner are on the way to becoming pro parents. Fatherhood is one of the best things that may happen to you, and I promise that every challenge has its reward. Put this opportunity to great use and do your best, but remember, even fourth-time fathers are still learning! Stay tuned for the next installment which will help get you through the first year of your child's life.

Now...a question for you! How do you feel after reading this book? Are you more at ease? Are you ready to jump in (or at least ready to dip your toe in?)? We'd love to know more about your thoughts on our first manual for new dads. Would you mind sharing an honest review? This can not only guide us in our creation of future books, but will also share valuable information with other soon-to-be fathers. Also, don't forget to join my Facebook group, First Time Father: A Men's Group for Dads and Dads-to-Be, to become part of an active and engaged community of Dad's just like you! Thank you, and we look forward to seeing you for our next installment, First Time Father: The New Dad's Modern Guide for Baby's First Year; An Easy-to-Follow Handbook to Thrive With Your Expanding Family.

DISCLAIMER. This book provides general information about pregnancy and prenatal issues. This information does not constitute medical advice and is not intended to be used as a solitary reference on the subject matter, for the diagnosis or treatment of a health problem, or as a substitute for consulting a licensed health care professional. Consult with a qualified physician or health care practitioner to discuss specific individual issues or health needs, and to professionally address personal, emotional, health, physical or medical concerns.

RESOURCES TO DIG DEEPER

GENERAL PREGNANCY INFORMATION - WEBSITES SPECIALIZING IN OBSTETRIC SUPPORT:

- What to Expect *www.whattoexpect.com*
- Mayo Clinic *www.mayoclinic.org*
- Center for Disease Control *https://www.cdc.gov/pregnancy/*
- American College of Obstetrics and Gynecology *acog.org*
- American Pregnancy Association *https://americanpregnancy.org/*
- Very Well Family (*https://www.verywellfamily.com/pregnancy-4157414* for all things pregnancy)

HEALTH & SAFETY

- Fish guide for pregnancy - *https://www. fda.gov/food/consumers/advice-about-eating-fish*
- Environmental Working Group - *https://www.ewg.org/,* *https://www. ewg.org/skindeep/*
- A parent's guide to first aid - *https://www.acls. net/a-parents-guide-to-first-aid*

SEX DURING PREGNANCY

- Dworkin-McDaniel, N. (2021, February 8). Sex during pregnancy: What every pregnant person should know. Parents. *https://www. parents.com/pregnancy/my-life/sex-relationship/pregnancy-sex-guide/*

FINANCIAL PREPARATION

- *youneedabudget.com*
- *hisandhermoney.com*
- *mommoneymap.com*
- Houston, R. (2019, July 24). Average cost of having a baby in 2022. SmartAsset;

SmartAsset. *https://smartasset.com/financial-advisor/cost-of-having-a-baby*

- Snider, S. (2019, August 29). Financial steps to take when you're pregnant. US News & World Report; U.S. News & World Report. *https://money.usnews.com/money/personal-finance/family-finance/articles/financial-steps-to-take-when-youre-pregnant*

Financial Apps

- Mint: *https://mint.intuit.com/*
- Daily Budget: *https://apps.apple.com/us/app/daily-budget-original/id651896614*
- HoneyFi: *https://www.honeyfi.com/*
- Mvelopes: *https://www.mvelopes.com/*
- Goodbudget: *https://goodbudget.com/*
- FamZoo: *https://famzoo.com/*
- Investopedia: *https://www.investopedia.com/*

PREPARING FOR BIRTH

- Immergut, D., & Graves, G. (2020, July 22). How to create your birth plan: A checklist for parents. Parents. *https://www.parents.com/*

pregnancy/giving-birth/labor-and-delivery/
checklist-how-to-write-a-birth-plan/

- Murkoff, H. (2018b, November 27). Choosing a childbirth class. What to Expect. *https://www.whattoexpect.com/pregnancy/* *childbirth-classes*

- Marple, K. (2021, January 12). Giving birth: What to pack in your hospital bag | babycenter. BabyCenter. *https://www.* *babycenter.com/pregnancy/your-body/packing-* *for-the-hospital-or-birth-center_185*

- Muennich, M. (n.d.). Men: A partner's guide to assisting during labour. MadeForMums. Retrieved May 19, 2021, from *https://www.* *madeformums.com/pregnancy/men-a-* *partners-guide-to-assisting-during-labour/*

Preparing for birth apps

- My Pregnancy Today: *https://www.* *babycenter.com/mobile-apps*
- 7 Best Pregnancy Apps for Dads including Labor and Contraction Timer: *https://www.* *parents.com/fun/entertainment/gadgets/best-* *apps-for-new-dads-dads-to-be/#page=5*

Preparing for Baby

- Today's Parent. (2020, January 7). Newborn checklist: Everything you need before your baby arrives. Today's Parent. *https://www. todaysparent.com/checklists/newborn-checklist/*
- Brown, S. (2003, November 11). How to change a baby's diaper. Verywell Family; Verywellfamily. *https://www.verywellfamily. com/how-to-change-a-diaper-289239*
- Lee, Y. (n.d.). Baby nursery checklist: 7 essential items & 5 things to forget. Money Crashers. Retrieved May 14, 2021, from *https://www.moneycrashers.com/baby-nursery-essentials-checklist/*
- Marcin, A. (2016, August 3). How to hold a newborn baby. Healthline; Healthline Media. *https://www.healthline.com/health/parenting/ how-to-hold-a-newborn#Step-4:-Choose-your-position*

Postpartum mental health

- *www.postpartum.net/*
- *www.postpartumdepression.org/resources/*

Breastfeeding

- La Leche League International *llli.org*
- The Breastfeeding Center for Greater Washington *breastfeedingcenter.org*

Made in the USA
Middletown, DE
24 June 2022